SIMPLE LEAVES

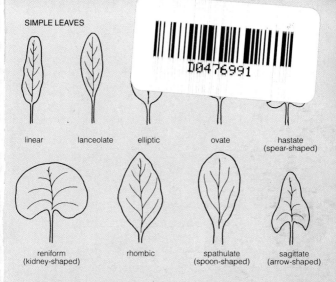

linear

lanceolate

elliptic

ovate

hastate
(spear-shaped)

reniform
(kidney-shaped)

rhombic

spathulate
(spoon-shaped)

sagittate
(arrow-shaped)

Warning

Poisonous and deadly species are clearly flagged, as are those that are
protected or endangered in all or part of their range. The text also
points out if there is any possibility of confusion with dangerous
species.

- Of those species suitable for use at home, only those that are
  not protected should be collected. In addition, avoid those with
  confusable similar species, especially since these may be
  dangerous. Always heed the specific warnings in the text.

- When making an identification, ensure that all parts of the
  description tally, and double check with the illustration. Even if
  just one detail seems uncertain, do not use the plant
  medicinally. If in doubt, consult an expert botanist before using.

- Collect wild plants very sparingly, never all from a single site.

Collins · NATURE GUIDE

HERBS AND HEALING PLANTS
OF BRITAIN & EUROPE

Dieter Podlech

Translated and adapted by
MARTIN WALTERS

Collins

Reprinted in 2011 for
Independent Book Sales

HarperCollins Publishers Ltd.
77-85 Fulham Palace Road
London W6 8JB

Collins is a registered trademark of
HarperCollins Publishers Ltd.

14

Written by Dieter Podlech
This edition translated and adapted by Martin Walters

Originally published in German as a GU Nature Guide
by Gräfe und Unzer GmbH, Munich

© Gräfe und Unzer GmbH, Munich, 1987
© in this English translation HarperCollins Publishers, 1996

ISBN-13: 978 0 26 167405 9

Collins uses papers that are natural, renewable and recyclable
products made from wood grown in sustainable forests. The
manufacturing processes conform to the environmental
regulations of the country of origin.

Printed and bound in China by South China Printing Company

How to use this book

This handy, lightweight guide is designed for everyone interested in medicinal plants, and is ideal for use in the field. It describes and illustrates the most important medicinal plants of Europe and the Mediterranean region. The 315 colour photographs, taken in their natural habitats, show the important features of each species, and many botanical drawings illustrate details such as flower structure, and stem and leaf shape.

The text covers all the important characters needed for identification, such as shape, flowering time, habitat and distribution, and also mentions similar species which might cause confusion. Information is also given about the active chemical constituents found in the plants, as well as the uses made of them in both conventional and homeopathic medicine. In addition, tips are provided for the home preparation and use of herbal remedies, where appropriate.

The drawings show either important features not visible in the photographs, or distinguishing characters of similar species. There are also drawings of leaf shapes and inflorescences (front-papers) and of flower shapes and fruit types (end-papers). The centimetre rule inside the cover will help you make measurements in the field.

There is a short botanical section (from p. 240), notes on collection, preparation and uses of medicinal plants, a summary of important active chemicals, and a calendar.

The scientific names of many herbs have the specific epithet (the second part of the Latin name) *officinalis*. This indicates their ancient use in herbal medicine. The word is derived from 'opificina', meaning a workshop or shop, which became shortened to 'officina', and came to mean a monastic store-room, a herb-store, and eventually a drug shop or pharmacy.

With careful use, this book enables even the entirely inexperienced to identify medicinal plants with ease. Readers are then able to learn about the active chemical substances they contain and the medicinal uses to which they are put.

Explanation of the symbols

☠ = poisonous

☒ = protected, endangered or threatened, at least in part of its range, therefore should not be collected

✿ = commonly grown in gardens or cultivated, often well outside its natural range

* = found wild in British Isles (whether native or introduced)

BI = British Isles

x = hybrid (in the Latin name)

Colour-coded identification

The method used here for identification is straightforward. The species illustrated and described are arranged in groups according to flower colour. Coloured thumb markers at the edges of the pages make it quick and easy to find these groups. Thus the first step in identification is to choose the colour section. The second step involves identifying the plant, using a combination of the colour photographs and the descriptions.

The botanical drawings of leaves, flowers, inflorescences and fruits provide extra help in identification. Within each colour group the species are arranged systematically, so that species in the same family or genus are treated close together.

COLOUR	PLANTS IN THAT GROUP	PAGE
	Blue contains all species with light to dark blue, or violet-blue flowers	8–27
	Yellow contains all species with light yellow to orange flowers	28–77
	Red contains all species with pink to dark red, purple or reddish-violet flowers	78–125
	White contains all species with white or cream flowers	126–191
	Green contains all species with greenish or brownish flowers	192–239

Exceptions to the rule

Most species can be successfully tracked down by their flower colour. There are, however, three particular (and rather rare) exceptions:

- Flowers that change colour during the flowering period (e.g. Lungwort, p.16, Hare's-foot Clover, p.86)
- Flowers that vary in colour – particularly red/blue (e.g. Common Mallow, p.92) and pale yellow/white (e.g. White Bryony, p.154).
- Species with two or more different colour forms (e.g. Common Comfrey, p.102)

The photographs

All the photographs are of species in their natural habitat, and show features such as the typical look of the plant, growth form at flowering time, stem leaves and, when important, basal leaves.

Plants are individuals, and their overall shape (largely genetically determined) can be influenced and altered by their environment. For this reason a plant will not always look exactly like its illustration.

The colour photographs and descriptions are arranged opposite each other on a single spread, each with the same number for ease of reference.

The descriptions

The characteristics of each species are described in detail. Flower colour is one of the most obvious distinguishing characters, and shape and flower type are the most valuable taxonomic features. The structure of the fruit is also important, as is leaf shape and arrangement. If the underground parts of a medicinal plant are intended for use, accurate identification must first be made on the basis of the above-ground parts.

A plant's **flowering season** is influenced by the weather and seasons, and by the precise site where it grows. For this reason the figures given encompass a relatively long period.

The information on **habitat** is often a useful pointer to identification, although most species can grow in a range of different conditions. The notes under **distribution** give an idea of the European (and sometimes world) range of each species.

The **active ingredients** found in each medicinal plant are listed, as are the main **uses** of the plant in both conventional and homeopathic medicine. Note however that these comments are made simply to provide information and are not intended as guidelines for home preparation or use.

Similar species are usually closely related plants which are used medicinally in similar fashion to the main species described. Some similar species are not of medicinal value. Indeed, they may even be dangerous (but note that many medicinal species are themselves poisonous!). If there is serious danger of confusion this is always noted in the text.

In cases where the plant may be used safely at home (most often as an infusion), **home use tips** are given. Unless otherwise indicated, please remember that the amounts (usually in teaspoons) refer to bought preparations of herbal drugs.

Conservation

You should not uproot **any** wild flower. Many rare species are specifically protected, and even common wild flowers may not be uprooted without permission. **Never pick any part of a protected species in the wild.**

Ideally, plants for use at home should be grown in a herb garden. If collected in the wild, only small quantities of common species should be used. Even common plants should not be taken unless they are abundant in that particular area.

1 # Saffron Crocus ✿ *Crocus sativus*
(Iris Family)

Perennial, 8–30 cm tall. Corm rather large, rounded with netted fibres. Leaves erect or spreading, narrowly linear, to 3 mm wide; green, with pale central stripe. Leaf margins and central keel on underside softly hairy. Flowers solitary, enclosed by 2 bracts towards base. Corolla-tube reaching down into the corm. Perianth pale violet, with darker or paler veins. Perianth lobes 6, narrowly elliptical, bearded inside towards base. Anthers yellow. Styles feathery, about 10 cm long, stigmas bright orange-red and 3-lobed, 2.5–3.5 cm long, gradually thickening towards tip. Does not set fruit.

Flowering season: Sep–Nov

Habitat: Known only in cultivation.

Distribution: Unknown.

Active ingredients: (Stigmas) glycosides, separable into pigments and bitters.

Uses: In homeopathy for treating bleeding, as a sedative and for treating depression. Also to reduce fevers and externally for bruises and rheumatism.

Further uses: Stigmas as a spice and colouring in cooking, particularly in baking and to flavour and colour rice. Used ceremonially in India.

NB: Beware confusion with the poisonous Meadow Saffron/Autumn Crocus (p. 78).

2 # Monk's-hood* ⚥ ✿ ☒ *Aconitum napellus*
(Buttercup Family)

Sturdy perennial, to about 1.5 m, with a tuberous root and powerful, usually unbranched stem. Leaves all up the stem, stalked and deeply divided, with 5–7 lobes; lobes themselves divided. Inflorescence a long, rather dense raceme. Flowers deep blue or mauve, stalked. Petals 5, unequal, the upper one curved over as a hood, and wider than long. Fruit a follicle with 3–5 seeds.

Flowering season: June–Aug

Habitat: High-altitude woodland, damp woods, river banks.

Distribution: Europe, north to Britain and S Sweden, often in upland areas.

Active ingredients: Aconitin and similar alkaloids.

Uses: In conventional medicine as a local anaesthetic; in homeopathy to treat fevers, neuralgia and certain heart conditions. In Chinese medicine for heart disease and treatment of uterine cancer.

NB: Deadly poisonous – do not collect or prepare.

Similar species: A. variegatum has blue, white or variegated flowers, and hoods taller than broad; pedicels hairless. C and S Europe. *A. lycoctonum* has long, tapering hoods. Most of Europe, except S and NW.

Liverleaf❋ ✿ ☒

Hepatica nobilis

(Buttercup Family)

To about 15 cm tall. Many basal leaves, often overwintering. Leaf-stems long and hairy. Leaves glossy green above, brownish-red to violet below, and 3-lobed. Flowers single and terminal, on long, hairy stalks. 3 sepal-like bracts beneath each flower. Flowers 2–3 cm across, with 5–10 violet or pink (sometimes white) perianth segments (petals and petal-like sepals). Stamens many. Fruits hairy.

Flowering season: Mar–Apr

Habitat: Deciduous woods, scrub, mainly on limestone.

Distribution: Widespread, except on acid soils. In BI introduced; naturalised in a few places.

Active ingredients: Protanemonin, anthocyanins, flavonoids, tannins.

Uses: In homeopathy for chronic bronchitis, throat infections and liver disorders.

NB: Protected species. Do not collect.

Pasqueflower❋ ☠✿ ☒

Pulsatilla vulgaris

(Buttercup Family)

Hairy plant, to 30 cm tall. Basal leaves (2–6) much divided, appearing after the flowers. Each stem has a single flower and a whorl of 3 feathery, leaf-like bracts. Flowers violet, about 5 cm long, at first bell-shaped, then opening out, hairy on the outside. Perianth segments (petaloid sepals) 6. Fruits to about 5 cm long, with hairy achenes and long, feathery styles.

Flowering season: Mar–May

Habitat: Dry grassland, mainly on chalk.

Distribution: C and W Europe, northwards to SE England (rare), Denmark and S Sweden.

Active ingredients: Protanemonin, which converts to the less poisonous anemonin on drying. Saponins, tannins.

Uses: In homeopathy to treat depression, migraine, complaints of the stomach and intestine, colds and skin rashes. Also for tension, earache and neuralgia.

Similar species: P. montana has smaller, darker flowers. It occurs on the mountains of C and SE Europe.

P. patens has wider leaf lobes. Mainly C and E Europe.

NB: All these species are poisonous and protected. Do not collect.

P. patens   P. vulgaris
Leaves

3

4

Sweet Violet*

Viola odorata

(Violet Family)

Sparsely hairy to glabrous stemless perennial, to 10 cm tall, with rooting stolons (creeping stems) to 20 cm long. Leaves stalked; stipules 1–4 times as long as they are wide. Leaves rounded, cordate, pubescent to almost glabrous. Flowers scented, pedicels pubescent towards base. Sepals 5, lanceolate, pointed, 5–7 mm, with basal appendages. Petals 5, dark violet, sometimes white, rarely pink, the lowest with short, nectar-filled spur. Fruit a 3-valved capsule.

Flowering season: Mar–Apr

Habitat: Open deciduous woods, woodland edges, scrub.

Distribution: S, C and W Europe. Only local in Scotland. Widespread, but often as a garden escape, and has many cultivated variants, some 'doubled'.

Active ingredients: Saponins, a glycoside; flowers have fragrant essential oil.

Uses: In homeopathy for earache, rheumatism, asthma and whooping cough.

Further uses: Flowers and leaves can be used in salads. Crystallised flowers used in sweets and liqueurs. Decocted flowers produce an antiseptic eyewash.

Home use tips: For bronchitis and coughs: 2 teaspoons in 250 ml cold water; bring to the boil and simmer, leave to infuse for 5 minutes. Drink 2–3 cups a day, sweetened with honey.

Flax* ⊛

Linum usitatissimum

(Flax Family)

Hairless annual, 30–80 cm tall, usually with erect stem, only branched in inflorescence. Leaves linear, narrow, alternate, pointed, to 4 cm. Flowers solitary and terminal on side branches. Sepals 5, lanceolate and pointed, 5–7 mm long, with 3–5 veins and white, whiskered margin. Petals 5, blue, obovate, 12–15 mm long. Stamens and the 5 styles blue. Fruit a rounded capsule with 10 valves. Seeds flat, shiny and brown, 5–6 mm long.

Flowering season: June–Aug

Habitat: As a crop or on wasteland.

Distribution: Cultivated origin. In BI casual; grown mainly in S England.

Active ingredients: Mucilage, pectin, oil rich in unsaturated fatty acids, linamarin.

Uses: Medically as mild laxative and to treat inflammation of stomach or intestine. The fatty acids in the oil can help remove heavy metals from the body and reduce risk of thrombosis. Externally as hot poultice for boils, swollen glands and sores. Linseed oil is used for chapped skin, eczema and shingles.

Further uses: Crop used for linen (tall cultivar) or linseed oil (short cultivar).

Home use tips: For constipation take 2 teaspoons of crushed seeds morning and evening. Treat boils, swollen glands and sores with hot linseed poultice. For chapped skin and shingles apply linseed oil (from chemist).

5

6
7

Dwarf Milkwort°

Polygala amarella

(Milkwort Family)

Almost glabrous perennial, 5–15 cm tall. Leaves alternate, narrowly obovate, narrowing and forming rosette towards base; upper stem leaves shorter and narrower than lower leaves. Inflorescence a terminal raceme of 10–40 flowers. Flowers short-stalked, in axils of small, frail bracts. The 2 lateral sepals (wings) are petal-like, elliptic, 2.5–4.5 mm long; the other 3 small. Petals 3, the lower ones fringed. Flowers small, blue, pink or white. Fruit a 2-seeded capsule.

Flowering season: May–July

Habitat: Meadows, wet flushes, damp, open woods; also calcareous grassland.

Distribution: N and C Europe and parts of Mediterranean region. Only local in England.

Active ingredients: Bitters, saponins, small amounts of essential oil and tannins.

Uses: To purify the blood.

Home use tips: To treat coughs and to purify the blood. Put 2 teaspoons in 250 ml cold water; bring to the boil and simmer. Drink 2–3 cups a day, sweetened with honey, for coughs.

Lesser Periwinkle° ☠⊛

Vinca minor

(Periwinkle Family)

Perennial, with long underground stems, rooting at nodes. Hairless, to about 20 cm tall. Flowering stems upright. Leaves in opposite pairs, ovate, short-stalked and evergreen, to about 5 cm long, pale green above, darker below. Flowers solitary and stalked, growing from leaf axils. Corolla 2–3 cm across, light blue, with short tube opening to a broad, flat face. Fruit (rarely produced in BI) of 2 follicles, joined at base.

Flowering season: Apr–May

Habitat: Deciduous woods, scrub; calcareous soils.

Distribution: Most of Europe, rarer towards the N; Caucasus, Turkey. Possibly native in S England; common in gardens.

Active ingredients: Alkaloids (vincamine, vincin, vincristine), bitters, flavonoids.

Uses: Circulatory disorders, especially of the brain. In homeopathy to treat bleeding and skin rashes.

Similar species: Greater Periwinkle° ⊛ (*V. major*) has larger flowers and wider, slightly heart-shaped leaves.

NB: Danger of overdose, therefore do not use at home.

8

9

Common Lungwort*

Pulmonaria officinalis

(Borage Family)

Hairy plant to about 35 cm, with white-spotted basal leaves, to about 15 cm long; petiole usually shorter than blade. Stem leaves alternate, elliptic, clasping stem. Flowers bell-shaped, 5-partite, starting out pink, then turning gradually violet or blue. Stamens enclosed by corolla-tube.

Flowering season: Mar–May

Habitat: Shady places, particularly on heavy, clay soils. Mixed woodland, scrub.

Distribution: C Europe, north to S Sweden and Holland. Introduced to Britain.

Active ingredients: Mucilage, saponin, bitters, vitamin C, minerals, silicic acid.

Uses: Leaves can be added to soup, and are also used in some vermouths. Leaves and stems are expectorant and diuretic. Soothe throat and lung complaints, and bronchitis. Lungwort helps check bleeding, and is also used for treating diarrhoea and haemorrhoids.

Home use tips: For coughs, sore throats, neckache, and as expectorant. Add 250 ml boiling water to 2 teaspoons of medicine. Leave to stand for 10 minutes. Take 3 times a day, sweetened with honey.

Similar species: Narrow-leaved Lungwort* (*P. longifolia*) has more slender leaves, often unspotted. Rather western, north to France and S England. Unspotted Lungwort (*P. obscura*) has unspotted leaves, with blade shorter than petiole. North to S Scandinavia.

Borage* ⊛

Borago officinalis

(Borage Family)

Roughly hairy annual, growing to 80 cm. Leaves alternate, growing as a rosette towards base, oval, to 10 cm long, often with irregularly toothed margin and winged petiole. Wings continued down stem in some of upper leaves. Inflorescence many-flowered, often spreading, almost umbel-like. Flowers on 2–4 cm long stalks, drooping. Calyx deeply 5-lobed, tips 1.5 cm long, widely spread in flower, later closing up. Corolla 2–3 cm across, with very short tube and 5 spreading, pointed lobes. Corolla tube with 5 lanceolate white projecting scales, which contrast with the blue petals. Fruits are ridged nutlets.

Flowering season: May–Sep

Habitat: Rough ground, wasteland, vineyards, rich soils.

Distribution: Mediterranean region. Introduced or grown as herb elsewhere; occasionally naturalised.

Active ingredients: Mucilage, starch, tannins, saponins, flavonoids, mineral salts.

Uses: In homeopathy for depression and nervous heart weakness. Reduces fever, and helps dry coughs. Seed oil used for menstrual problems, irritable bowel syndrome, eczema, arthritis, and to ease hangovers.

Further uses: In salads and with vegetables. Leaves used to flavour drinks (resemble cucumber in taste).

12   **Chaste Tree**   *Vitex agnus-castus*

(Verbena Family)

Shrub, 3–5 m tall. Leaves opposite, long-stalked, palmate, mostly with 5–7 narrow, pointed leaflets. Leaflets dark green above, with felty white hairs beneath. Flowers small and clustered in branching panicles. Calyx bell-shaped, 5-lobed. Corolla tube-shaped, with 2 lips, 6–9 mm long, hairy on the outside, with a 3-lobed lower lip and divided upper lip. Fruit a fleshy berry, 3–5 mm, reddish-black when ripe (resembles peppercorn).

Flowering season: June–Sep

Habitat: River banks, damp places; always close to water-table.

Distribution: Mediterranean region; also planted as a decorative species.

Active ingredients: Essential oil, saponins, iridoid glycosides.

Uses: Yields drugs used in treating eyes. Reputedly used to decrease sexual desire (hence Chaste Tree). Homeopathic treatment for male potency disorders.

Note: The related Chinese species *Vitex negundo* is used in traditional Chinese medicine against malaria, coughs and bacterial dysentery.

13   **Sage** ⊛   *Salvia officinalis*

(Mint Family)

Aromatic shrub with softly hairy leaves, growing to about 70 cm. Leaves opposite, stalked, narrowly elliptic, with finely toothed margin and wrinkled below. Flowers in whorls of 4–8, in terminal, interrupted spikes. Calyx tubular or bell-shaped, 5-toothed. Corolla 2–3 cm, distinctly 2-lipped.

Flowering season: May–July

Habitat: Dry slopes.

Distribution: Mediterranean region. Often cultivated.

Active ingredients: Essential oil, tannin, bitters, flavonoids.

Uses: In homeopathy as anti-perspirant, and for mouth and throat infections. Leaf tea used as an antiseptic nerve and blood tonic.

Further uses: As herb in soups, vegetables and roasts, and in stuffing for poultry.

Home use tips: As gargle for mouth and throat. Put 1–2 teaspoons in 250 ml cold water; bring to the boil and simmer.

14   **Meadow Clary*** ⊛ ☒   *Salvia pratensis*

(Mint Family)

Softly hairy plant to about 1 m. Square-stemmed. Basal leaves in a rosette, with a long stalk and irregular teeth. Stem leaves fewer and smaller, growing close to stem. Loose long spikes of whorled violet-blue flowers. Corolla to about 3 cm, sickle-shaped and much longer than calyx.

Flowering season: May–Aug

Habitat: Dry grassland, hay meadows, grassy paths.

Distribution: S and C Europe, north to N Germany and S England (rare in latter); Turkey, Caucasus, N Africa, N America.

Active ingredients and uses: As for Sage, but less effective. The name comes from the Latin 'clarus', clear, and this herb was used to clear the sight.

Similar species: Wild Clary°, *S. verbenaca*, is smaller, with blue to violet flowers, and stickily hairy calyx. SE England and W France.

Clary° ⊛ (*S. sclarea*) of S Europe, is introduced to S Britain. It has pink or white bracts. Flower- and leaf-water used to treat tired eyes. Oil used in aromatherapy.

12

13

14

Rosemary* ⚜

Rosmarinus officinalis

(Mint Family)

Evergreen shrub to 2 m tall. Leaves opposite and almost sessile, narrowly linear, green above, grey-white below, with downrolled edges. Flowers in groups of 5–10, clustered on shoots. Calyx bell-shaped, 2-lipped, brownish-green. Corolla blue-violet, rarely white, 2-lipped. Upper lip somewhat recurved and 2-lobed, lower lip with large central lobe and 2 side-lobes. Stamens 2.

Flowering season: Jan–Dec

Habitat: Dry sites near coast; maquis.

Distribution: Mediterranean. In BI, introduced, mainly in S England.

Active ingredients: Essential oil, resin, tannins, flavonoids, bitters.

Uses: Externally as a rub or added to bath water to treat rheumatism, gout, and circulatory disorders; also in shampoo. Oil is anti-bacterial and anti-fungal.

Further uses: As culinary herb.

Home use tips: To treat exhaustion, especially after infection. Add 1 teaspoonful to 250 ml cold water; slowly bring to the boil and simmer. Drink 1 cup each morning and afternoon. Boil 50 g in 1 l water and leave for 30 minutes to prepare some extract for a bath.

Lavender/Common Lavender ⊕

(Mint Family)

Lavandula angustifolia

Branching shrubby evergreen perennial, 20–60 cm tall with narrow, opposite leaves about 8 times as long as they are wide. Young leaves white-tomentose, grey-green when older. Flowers in spikes, grouped in whorls. Bracts oval, bearded. Calyx grey-violet, tubular, with very short teeth. Corolla 1 cm long, softly hairy, 2-lipped, with long upper lip and shorter lower lip. Stamens 4, enclosed in corolla tube.

Flowering season: June-Aug

Habitat: Warm, dry sites.

Distribution: Mediterranean.

Active ingredients: Essential oil, tannins.

Uses: Sedative. Used to treat migraines, exhaustion, and nervous disorders of the heart (as an infusion or a bath). Oil to treat insect bites, burns and sore throats.

Further uses: Oil used in perfume industry (best oil from Common and French Lavenders). Flowers to flavour preserves, sweets and stews; dried in pot-pourri. Lavender water as skin tonic and antiseptic.

Home use tips: As for Rosemary.

Similar species: Spike Lavender ⊕ (*L. latifolia*) has silver-grey leaves, only 4–6 times as long as they are wide. Dry sites in W Mediterranean. French Lavender ⊕ (*L. stoechas*) has large upright, purple bracts. S Mediterranean and N Africa.

Note: The most commonly planted form (at least in BI) is Garden Lavender* ⊕ (*L.* x *intermedia*) a hybrid between *L. angustifolia* and *L. latifolia*. It is occasionally found as a casual.

15

16

17

18 Hyssop ✽

(Mint Family)

Hyssopus officinalis

Semi-evergreen, aromatic sub-shrub with branched stems to 1.5 m tall.
Leaves opposite, almost sessile, narrowly lanceolate, glandular on both
surfaces. Flowers with very short stalks, in rather lop-sided spikes, made up
of whorled clusters of 3–7 flowers. Calyx tubular, with lanceolate, bearded
teeth. Corolla 8–12 mm long, tubular, with short, flat upper lip (hairy on
outside) and longer, 3-lobed lower lip. Stamens 4, longer than corolla; style
even longer.

Flowering season: Aug–Oct

Habitat: Dry rocks, and calcareous scree.

Distribution: Mediterranean region. Introduced further N (including BI).
Naturalised in some parts of C Europe.

Active ingredients: Essential oil, tannins, bitter glycosides.

Uses: As infusion for treating flu, bronchitis and catarrh. As poultice for
bruises.

Further uses: As culinary herb, especially with meat, beans, soups and
salads. Also as flavouring in liqueurs.

Home use tips: As expectorant for coughs and throat infections, flatulence
and indigestion. Boil 2 teaspoons in 250 ml water, and infuse for 5 minutes.
Drink 2 cups daily.

19 Ground-ivy*

(Mint Family)

Glechoma hederacea

Creeping plant to about 20 cm tall, rooting at the nodes, with erect, square
flowering stems. Smells rather unpleasant. Rounded blunt-toothed
opposite leaves, on long stalks. Flowers paired or in threes, in leaf axils.
Corolla 1–2 cm long, blue-violet or lilac, 2-lipped (lower lip divided into 3).
Calyx with short hairs, 4–7 mm long, 5-toothed and weakly 2-lipped, often
shot with violet.

Flowering season: Apr–July

Habitat: Deciduous damp woodland, scrub, woodland edges, meadows.

Distribution: Most of Europe; Caucasus, Siberia.

Active ingredients: Bitters, tannins, essential oils, saponins, organic acids,
vitamin C.

Uses: As blood cleanser, tonic and diuretic, and to treat cystitis, gastritis and
kidney stones. The leaves are said to reduce inflammation.

Further uses: As a herb, added to spring salads and vegetables. Formerly
used to clarify beer and improve its flavour (was called Ale-hoof).

Home use tips: For loss of appetite, diarrhoea, coughs and as expectorant.
Add 250 ml boiling water to 1–2 teaspoons of medicine. Leave to stand for
5 minutes. Take 3 cups a day.

18

19

20 Heath (Common) Speedwell*

(Figwort Family) *Veronica officinalis*

Perennial, to 20 cm tall. Stems to 30 cm long, hairy and low-growing, turning upwards towards the end, with erect inflorescences, and rooting at nodes. Leaves opposite, short-stalked, broadly lanceolate to oval, softly hairy and finely toothed. Inflorescence a raceme in axil of upper leaves. Flowers 1–3 mm long, stalked. Calyx 4-partite, with glandular hairs. Corolla open, 4-lobed, 6–7 mm across, pale lilac (rarely white) with dark veins. Fruit a laterally compressed heart-shaped capsule, 3–4 mm long and wide, with glandular hairs. Style about as long as the fruit.

Flowering season: June–Aug

Habitat: Heaths, dry grassland and open woods, woodland edges, poor pasture.

Distribution: Europe, N Asia, North America. Common throughout BI.

Active ingredients: Tannins, bitters, some essential oil, and the glycoside aucubin.

Home use tips: For digestive problems, diarrhoea, coughs and colds, and as gargle for mouth and throat infections. Boil 2 teaspoons in 250 ml water, infuse for 10 minutes. Drink 3 cups daily.

21 Devil's-bit Scabious*

Succisa pratensis

(Teasel Family)

Perennial to about 80 cm tall, with softly hairy stems, usually branching towards top. Root short and truncated. The Devil is supposed to have bitten it off to destroy the plant's medicinal properties. Basal leaves broadly lanceolate, stem leaves stalkless. Flowering heads about 1.5–2.5 cm across, compact, and violet-blue, with lanceolate bracts. Calyx with bristly teeth. Each flower has 4-lobed violet-blue corolla. Epicalyx 4-toothed. Calyx with bristles. Fruit 5–7 mm long, rectangular and hairy, with 8 furrows.

Flowering season: July–Sep

Habitat: Fens, meadows, poor grassland.

Distribution: Europe, W Siberia, NW Africa.

Active ingredients: Saponins, tannins.

Uses: In homeopathy for skin complaints.

Home use tips: An expectorant syrup to relieve respiratory complaints. Bring 2 teaspoons to the boil in 250 ml water, and simmer for a minute. Dissolve as much brown sugar as possible into it, and add 2 teaspoons of honey. Take 2 teaspoonsful, twice a day.

20

21

Cornflower* ⊕🏵☒

Centaurea cyanus

(Daisy Family)

Annual or biennial, growing to about 80 cm. Stem with felty hairs and branching towards top. Leaves narrow, the lower ones sometimes divided and usually drying off before flowers appear. Solitary blue flowerheads; outer florets blue and inner florets reddish. Bracts green with black triangular markings and fringed margins. Corollas broaden towards outside of flower head. Fruits 3.5 mm long, with rust-brown bristly pappus about 2–3 mm long.

Flowering season: June–Oct

Habitat: A weed of grain crops and waste ground.

Distribution: Europe. Has declined throughout region. Now virtually extinct in the wild in Britain, but often grown in gardens.

Active ingredients: Mucilage, pigments, tannins, bitters.

Uses: Earlier to treat loss of appetite and digestive disorders, and also as a diuretic. Now mainly as an additive to infusions. Flower infusion as hair and skin tonic and for treating conjunctivitis. Stimulates digestion.

Similar species: Perennial Cornflower* ⊕☒ (*C. montana*) has winged stem and broader leaves (upper decurrent). Inner flowers of head violet, asymmetrical and tube-shaped, outer flowers larger and blue. Woodland and scrub, grassland, rough ground. Found in mountains of C and S Europe. Introduced to BI, and naturalised. Active ingredients and uses as for Cornflower.

NB: Both species are becoming rarer and should not be collected.

Chicory* 🏵

Cichorium intybus

(Daisy Family)

Perennial to 1.2 m tall, with branched stem and milky sap. Basal leaves lanceolate, mostly deeply divided and roughly hairy beneath; stem leaves small. Flowerheads 3–5 cm across, in the axils of bracts. Corollas all of ray type and pale blue. Involucre cylindrical; outer bracts short and sticking out, inner ones upright. Fruit pale brown, 2–2.5 mm long, with very short pappus.

Flowering season: July–Oct

Habitat: Roadsides and waste places, pasture.

Distribution: Most of Europe, Middle East, NW Africa. Frequent (possibly native) in England and Wales, rare in Scotland and Ireland. Widely introduced.

Active ingredients: Bitters, choline, tannins.

Uses: In homeopathy as an appetite stimulant, and to treat flatulence and stomach pains.

Further uses: One cultivated form has a swollen root, which is roasted to yield chicory-coffee. Root chicories are also used as a root vegetable. Several varieties are used as vegetables, including Belgian Chicory whose bud-shaped heads (chicons) are eaten cooked or raw, and Catalonia Chicory, common in S Italy. There are also broad-leaved lettuce-like forms, such as the Radicchios.

Home use tips: For loss of appetite. Put 1 teaspoonful in 250 ml water; bring to the boil and simmer for 2–3 minutes. Drink 2–3 cups a day.

Similar species: Endive ⊕ (C. endivia) is very similar, but has hairless, less deeply lobed leaves. As with Chichory, there are cultivated forms, notably Escarole and Scarole (e.g. Batavian Endive). The bitter leaves are cooked or used in salads.

22

23

Asparagus*

Asparagus officinalis

(Lily Family)

Hairless perennial, 30–100 cm tall (to 1.5 m in cultivation). Stem erect, branching. The leaves are small, pale and scale-like, and their function is taken over by the needle-like cladodes (modified stems) which grow in clusters in the scale-leaf axils. Male and female flowers usually on separate plants. Perianth yellowish, bell- or funnel-shaped and 6-lobed. Male flowers about 5 mm long, female flowers rather shorter. Fruit a pea-sized, bright-red berry.

Flowering season: Apr–May

Habitat: Sandy fields, dunes, vineyards, river banks.

Distribution: See note below.

Active ingredients: Asparagin, arginine, saponins, flavonoids, sugar, fat, vitamins.

Uses: As infusion for treating bladder and kidney complaints.

Further uses: Young shoots (spears) as a vegetable, and in soup.

Home use tips: For urine retention, and bladder and kidney infection. Put 2 teaspoonsful of asparagus root in 250 ml water; bring to the boil and simmer. Drink 2–3 cups a day, but do not continue for more than a week.

Note: The Garden Asparagus* ⊕ is *A. officinalis* ssp. *officinalis*, native to C and S Europe, N Africa and W and C Asia. In BI it is introduced and naturalised in some places, notably E Anglian heaths and coastal dunes. Wild Asparagus* is *A. officinalis* ssp. *prostratus*, which is native on grassy sea-cliffs in BI, but rather rare and local. Asparagus 'fern' sold as decoration by florists is a South African species, *A. plumosus*.

Birthwort* ⚥☒

Aristolochia clematitis

(Birthwort Family)

Perennial to 1 m tall, with upright, unbranched stem. Leaves stalked, heart-shaped, about as long as they are broad, with obvious veins spreading out from stalk, matt green above, pale green below. Flowers in clusters in the leaf axils, erect when opened. Perianth zygomorphic, 3–5 cm long, yellow, inflated towards base and narrowing to a lipped tube at the top. Fruit a hanging, somewhat pear-shaped capsule.

Flowering season: May–June

Habitat: Open woodland, scrub, walls, vineyards.

Distribution: Central Europe (mainly in wine-growing areas), Mediterranean, Turkey, Caucasus. In Britain rare and scattered (introduced).

Active ingredients: Essential oil, bitters, antibiotic substances.

Uses: Used formerly to treat infections and in earlier homeopathy for frost-bite, acne, eczema, circulatory, menstrual and intestinal disorders.

NB: Contains a carcinogenic substance. Do not collect or use.

Note: The related Chinese Fairy Vine (*A. debilis*) is used to treat snake bites, stomach pains and sore throats. It also has pain-killing and tumour-reducing agents.

Sweet Bay/Bay Laurel* ⊛

Laurus nobilis

(Laurel Family)

Evergreen shrub or small tree to about 20 m tall, with blackish bark.
Leaves alternate, lanceolate, 5–15 cm long, leathery and dark green, usually
with entire, somewhat wavy margins. Strongly aromatic when crushed.
Plant dioecious. Flowers 4-partite, pale yellow, in small clusters. Male
flowers have 10–12 bright yellow anthers, usually each with 2 glands at
base. Female flowers with 4 sterile stamens. Fruit a black berry, 2 cm long.
Flowering season: Mar–Apr
Habitat: Warm Mediterranean woods and scrub.
Distribution: Mediterranean coasts. In BI planted and naturalised in some
areas, notably SW Britain and SW Ireland.
Habitat: Maquis and scrub. Often planted in gardens as an
ornamental plant or herb. Frost-sensitive.
Active ingredients: Essential oils, fatty oil, bitters.
Uses: Now oil from leaves and fruits just used externally for treating sores.
In veterinary medicine used for sore udders, sprains and pulled muscles.
Leaf essence in bath water relieves aching limbs.
Further uses: Leaves as culinary herb, e.g. for sauces, soups, pâtés, stews
and marinades. Oil used in some liqueurs.

Barberry* ⊛

Berberis vulgaris

(Barberry Family)

Thorny shrub to 3 m tall, with pale green to pale grey bark. Stems with
0.5–3 cm long 3-partite spines. Short shoots in spine axils, with groups of
leaves. Leaves short-stalked, elliptic to obovate, 2–6 cm long; margins with
small slightly spiny teeth. Stalked flowers in loose, usually drooping,
racemes. Perianth of side flowers 6-partite, terminal flowers 5-partite.
Sepaloid perianth segments small and yellow; petaloid segments oval,
5–6 mm long. Stamens 6. Fruit a red few-seeded berry, 8–11 mm long.
Flowering season: May–June
Habitat: Open deciduous woods, scrub.
Distribution: Central Europe, N Mediterranean region, Turkey. In BI
probably introduced, but naturalised.
Active ingredients: Alkaloids, tannins.
Uses: In homeopathy for gall-bladder problems, colic, jaundice, nephritis,
pyelitis and rheumatic joints.
Further uses: The vitamin-rich edible fruits stimulate the appetite and are
used to make juice and jam.

**NB: Apart from the berries, all parts of the plant are poisonous. Do
not collect, or use at home.**

31 Wolf's-bane* ⊛ ☠   *Aconitum vulparia*

(Buttercup Family)

Perennial, to 1 m tall, with root only slightly thickened. Lower leaves with
long stalks and blade divided (but not to base) into 5 coarsely toothed lobes;
about 15 cm broad, sparsely hairy below. Stem leaves 1–3, similar but
smaller. Flowers in loose racemes, in leaf axils; strongly zygomorphic.
Upper perianth segment forms tall hood, the other 4 being oval. Stamens
many. Fruit consists of 3–5 many-seeded follicles.

Flowering season: June–Aug

Habitat: Damp mountain woodland, tall-herb communities.

Distribution: Mountains of C and S Europe. In BI introduced, occasionally
naturalised.

Active ingredients: Alkaloids.

Uses: In homeopathy (rare) for tonsillitis and glandular problems.

Further uses: Used at one time to poison wolves (hence name; 'bane' =
poison).

NB: Deadly poisonous. Do not collect or use at home.

32 Marsh Marigold* ⊛ ☠   *Caltha palustris*

(Buttercup Family)

Hairless perennial, to 50 cm tall. Stem low-growing or curving upwards to
erect, hollow and branching towards top. Lower leaves broad (5–10 cm
across), shiny, toothed and heart-shaped with long stalks. Upper stem
leaves similar, but smaller and unstalked. Flowers solitary and terminal on
side branches, bright shiny yellow, 5-partite, to 5 cm across. Stamens many.
Fruits are many-seeded follicles, to 2.5 cm long, in a star-shaped cluster.

Flowering season: Mar–Apr

Habitat: Streamsides, wet meadows and wet woodland.

Distribution: Europe, N Asia, N America.

Active ingredients: Saponins, flavonoids, choline.

Uses: In homeopathy for treating blistery rashes, whooping cough,
bronchial catarrh and menstrual problems.

Further uses: Green buds sometimes used in salted vinegar as a caper
substitute.

NB: Fresh plant is at least mildly poisonous. Use not recommended.

33 Lesser Celandine* ⊛   *Ranunculus ficaria*

(Buttercup Family)

Hairless plant growing to 30 cm tall, with creeping stems, rooting at nodes. Leaves heart-shaped and fleshy, with wavy margins and long stalks. May have bulbils in axils of stem leaves. Flowers yellow (fading to white) 2–3 cm across, with 3–7 sepals and 8–12 long petals. Fruits are hairy achenes, 2–2.5 mm long, with straight beak.

Flowering season: Mar–May

Habitat: Deciduous woods, scrub, damp meadows.

Distribution: Europe, except Iceland and much of Scandinavia; N Africa, Asia, Caucasus.

Active ingredients: Protanemonin, anemonin, saponin.

Uses: Young plants as part of spring salad (said to purify the blood).

NB: Do not use too much because of the (albeit small) quantities of protanemonin, which can be harmful.

34 Celery-leaved Buttercup* ☠

(Buttercup Family)   *Ranunculus sceleratus*

Hairless, to 1 m tall. Leaves deeply 3-lobed; lobes narrowly lanceolate with entire or roughly toothed margin. Lower leaves stalked, upper leaves sessile. Flowers 5-partite, 0.5–1 cm across. Sepals 2–4 mm long, falling early. Petals slightly shorter than calyx. Fruits rounded and flattened achenes, 0.8–1 mm across, with very short, straight beak.

Flowering season: June–Nov

Habitat: Ditches, ponds, streamsides, in mud.

Distribution: Most of Europe and Asia. In BI mainly in England; scattered and mainly coastal in Scotland, Wales and Ireland.

Active ingredients: Protanemonin, anemonin.

Uses: In homeopathy to treat rheumatism, pancreatic disorders, skin rashes, central nervous system.

NB: Very poisonous. Do not collect or use at home.

35 Yellow Pheasant's-eye ☠ ⊛ ☒

(Buttercup Family)   *Adonis vernalis*

To 50 cm. Leaves all stalked and feathery, with pointed tips. Flowers solitary, yellow, to about 7 cm across. Sepals broadly oval and hairy. Petals (10–20) long and oval, sometimes toothed at end and golden yellow. Fruits (nutlets) to 5 mm, hairy with hooked beak.

Flowering season: Apr–May

Habitat: Heathy grassland, open pine woods, mainly on calcareous, but also on sandy soils.

Distribution: From Spain to Sweden, reaching SE Europe and Urals. Rare in C Europe. Absent from BI.

Active ingredients: Cardiac glycosides, flavoglycosides.

Uses: To strengthen heartbeat. In homeopathy for heart complaints and for overactive thyroid.

NB: Plant poisonous and protected. Do not collect or use at home.

36   Greater Celandine* ✄   *Chelidonium majus*

(Poppy Family)

Perennial to 1 m tall, with upright, branching stem, bristly hairs and bright orange, milky sap. Leaves alternate (lower leaves stalked, upper leaves sessile), green above, blue-green beneath, pinnate, with oval, toothed lobes. Flowers yellow, 2–3 cm across; sepals 2, falling early. Petals 4, equal and oval. Stamens numerous, anthers club-shaped. Fruit a 2–5 cm long capsule.

Flowering season: May–Oct

Habitat: Waste ground, footpaths, walls, scrub, open woods and parks.

Distribution: Most of Europe, except far N. Introduced in many areas, including most if not all of BI. Asia, N Africa.

Active ingredients: Alkaloids, saponins.

Uses: In conventional and homeopathic medicine for stomach, intestine and liver problems. Also by herbalists to treat jaundice and rheumatoid swelling. Sap used as ancient remedy for corns, ringworm fungus, verrucas and warts.

NB: Poisonous. Do not use at home.

37   White Mustard*   *Sinapis alba*

(Cabbage Family)

Annual to 80 cm tall, hairy below. Leaves stalked, lobed or pinnate, narrower towards top of plant. Flowers in racemes. Sepals 4–6 mm long; petals 7–10 mm long, yellow. Fruits erect to horizontal, 2.5–4 cm long, with obvious beak and many long, stiff hairs.

Flowering season: June–Oct

Habitat: Arable land, waste ground, footpaths.

Distribution: Europe, except extreme N. Introduced in BI.

Active ingredients: Glycosides, sinapine, fatty oil.

Uses: To make American mustard (from seeds); added to some other kinds of mustard. Some forms for use as seedlings in salads.

Home use tips: Take 1 teaspoonful of crushed seeds daily to improve digestion.

Similar species: Charlock° (*S. arvensis*), has unlobed or less deeply lobed leaves. This common weed has bright yellow flowers. Rape° ✲ (*Brassica napus*) is a common escape. About 1 m tall, with larger yellow flowers.

38   Black Mustard* ✲   *Brassica nigra*

(Cabbage Family)

Annual to 1.2 m tall, hairy at base. Leaves stalked and irregularly toothed or pinnate; upper stem leaves entire. Flowers in racemes. Sepals 3.5–4.5 mm long. Petals 7.5–9 mm long. Fruit smooth, borne erect, 1–2 cm long, beak 1.5–3 mm.

Flowering season: June–Sep

Habitat: Fields, footpaths, waste ground.

Distribution: Europe, Asia. In BI probably native. Ancient cultivated plant in Mediterranean region.

Active ingredients: Glycosides, sinigrin, sinapin, fatty oil.

Uses: As appetite stimulant and to aid digestion. For circulation, rheumatism, gout and catarrh. In homeopathy for colds, sore throats and bronchial catarrh.

Further uses: Leaves may be cooked, like spinach, or put in salads when young.

Home use tips: For rheumatism and the circulation. Mix 100 g powdered seeds into paste with luke-warm water, smear onto linen bandage, apply for 10 mins.

37

39 Biting Stonecrop*

Sedum acre

(Stonecrop Family)

Hairless mat-forming plant to 15 cm tall. Non-flowering stems with thick covering of oval, fleshy leaves. Leaves flat-topped and rounded below, to 4 mm long, sharp-tasting. Flowers 5-partite. Sepals short and oval, about 3 mm long. Petals lanceolate, pointed, almost horizontal and 7–10 mm long, yellow. Stamens 10. Fruits are follicles spreading in star-shape, 3–5 mm long.

Flowering season: June–Aug

Habitat: Rocks, dry grassland, walls, waste ground.

Distribution: Most of Europe; N Africa; Asia.

Active ingredients: Alkaloids, tannins, rutin.

Uses: In homeopathy to treat piles. Also for warts and corns.

Further uses: Gives a good peppery flavour to salads.

Similar species: Tasteless Stonecrop* (*S. sexangulare*) has no sharp taste. Leaves cylindrical, to 6 mm long, 1 mm thick, with short spur at base. Mainland Europe, naturalised in a few places in Britain.

40 Agrimony*

Agrimonia eupatoria

(Rose Family)

Upright plant, to 1.5 m tall, covered with soft hairs. Leaves pinnate, the larger leaflets having smaller leaflets between them. Leaflets toothed. Flowers yellow, on very short stalks. Receptacle goblet-shaped, with 10 longitudinal furrows, with hooked bristles. Petals narrowly obovate, 4–6 mm long. Fruit deeply grooved, nodding.

Flowering season: June–Sep

Habitat: Open woods, hedges, meadows; usually on calcareous soils.

Distribution: Most of Europe. Rare in N Scotland.

Active ingredients: Tannins, bitters, essential oil.

Uses: To treat complaints of stomach, intestine, gallbladder and liver. Extracts seem to inhibit certain bacteria and viruses.

Note: The related Chinese *A. pilosa* contains a blood coagulant, and inhibits some types of cancer.

Home use tips: For throat infections. Put 2 teaspoonsful in 250 ml boiling water. Leave to infuse for 10 minutes. Gargle several times a day.

Similar species: Fragrant Agrimony* (*A. procera*) has aromatic glands on the stems and leaves (*A. eupatoria* often fragrant too) and leafier stems.

41 Wood Avens*

Geum urbanum

(Rose Family)

Also known as Herb Bennet. A rather straggly plant to 60 cm tall, with hairy stems and pinnate, long-stalked leaves. The yellow, open flowers are solitary and terminal on side branches. Similar to cinquefoil flowers, but rather small and inconspicuous. These turn into tight, slightly prickly fruit-heads.

Flowering season: May–Oct

Habitat: Damp woods, scrub, hedges.

Distribution: Throughout Europe. In BI absent from N Scotland.

Active ingredients: Essential oils, tannins, bitters.

Uses: Treats fevers and diarrhoea; also piles. As gargle for sore throats.

Further uses: As alcoholic drink flavouring. Leaves added to salads and soups.

42 # Silverweed*   *Potentilla anserina*

(Rose Family)

Hairy perennial to 15 cm tall, with long, creeping stems, rooting at the nodes. Basal leaves to 20 cm long, pinnate, with toothed leaflets. Leaflets almost smooth above, silvery hairy beneath. Flowers solitary and long-stalked, with 5 petals, borne in leaf-axils, and 2–3 cm across. Epicalyx silkily hairy, segments often toothed. Sepals of equal length, pointed, mostly undivided. Petals twice as long as sepals. Stamens 20. Fruit a head of achenes.

Flowering season: May–Aug

Habitat: Meadows, footpaths, waste land.

Distribution: Almost worldwide.

Active ingredients: Tannins, flavonoids, an as yet unidentified relaxant.

Uses: To treat menstrual disorders and colic-like stomach and intestinal complaints. Also diarrhoea and gall-bladder problems. In homeopathy for menstrual disorders and as a relaxant.

Further uses: Flowers reduce bleeding and inflammation, and are antiseptic. Gargle for sore throats, and as wash for sunburn. The root is edible, but not very tasty.

Home use tips: For cramp-like stomach and indigestion pains. Infuse 2 teaspoonsful in boiling water for 10 minutes. Drink 2–3 cups daily.

43 # Tormentil*   *Potentilla erecta*

(Rose Family)

Hairy perennial, to 30 cm tall with basal leaf rosette. Basal leaves usually withered by flowering time. Rootstock knobbly, dark brown outside and blood-red inside. Stems erect. Stem leaves trifoliate, but appearing 5-digitate because of leaflet-like stipules. Leaflets toothed from middle onwards. Flowers stalked, mostly with 4 petals, about 1 cm across. Epicalyx present. Petals a little longer than sepals. Stamens 15–20. Fruits small (4–20).

Flowering season: May–Oct

Habitat: Meadows, bogs, heaths.

Distribution: Europe; Asia; N Africa.

Active ingredients: Tannins.

Uses: To treat stomach and intestine problems, also diarrhoea. Externally as gargle for mouth and throat infections, and to treat piles.

Further uses: Root said to stimulate the immune system.

Home use tips: For stomach problems and diarrhoea. Also as gargle for mouth and throat infections, and for treating wounds and frost-bite. Boil 1–3 dessert spoonsful in water for 15 minutes. As internal medicine 3 cups daily. Externally as gargle or compress.

42

43

44 Broom* ☠ — *Cytisus scoparius*
(Pea Family)

Branched shrub, to 2 m tall. Stems mostly upright, first bright green, then blackish, 5-ridged and branching. Leaves alternate and mostly falling early, trifoliate and stalked on older stems, stalkless and simple on young stems. Leaflets elliptical or obovate, to 2 cm long, dark green, bare or with appressed hairs. Flowers delicately scented, solitary or paired in leaf axils. Flower stalk twice as long as short, bell-shaped, 2-lipped calyx. Cleft between 2 lips deeper than that in upper lip. Corolla yellow, pea-like, 2–2.5 cm long; all petals of similar length. Fruit a pod, to over 4 cm long, flat, hairy only at edges; black when ripe.

Flowering season: May–June

Habitat: Heaths, open woodland, clearings, scrub; often planted by roads; avoids calcareous soils.

Distribution: W, S and C Europe, rarer towards E and N (frost sensitive).

Active ingredients: Alkaloids, notably spartein, tannins, flavoglycosides.

Uses: To treat heart muscle and some other cardiac problems; also bleeding. In homeopathy to treat irregular heart rhythms.

Further uses: Flexible twigs sometimes used to make brooms. The flowers are edible, buds can be eaten in salads, and wine made from open flowers.

NB: Most parts poisonous. Do not collect or use. Beware confusion with Spanish Broom (*Spartium junceum*) which is even more poisonous.

45 Dyer's Greenweed* — *Genista tinctoria*
(Pea Family)

Sparsely hairy plant to 1 m tall, with erect, spineless twigs. Leaves lanceolate. Flowers golden yellow, in lateral clusters or terminal racemes, each 1–1.5 cm long. Calyx 2-lipped; cleft between the 2 lips no deeper than that in upper lip. Fruit a narrow, flattened pod, 1.5–2.5 cm long, usually hairless.

Flowering season: June–Sep

Habitat: Heaths, pastures, scrub, open woods

Distribution: Most of Europe, except N Scandinavia; Asia.

Active ingredients: Alkaloids, tannins, flavonoids.

Uses: In medicine (rarely used) for rheumatism, gout, as diuretic, for urinary infections and kidney stones.

Further uses: Used as a source of yellow dye hence common name.

NB: Not recommended; side-effects as yet insufficiently researched.

46 Ribbed (Common) Melilot* — *Melilotus officinalis*
(Pea Family)

Erect plant with trifoliate leaves, to 1.5 m. Leaflets with toothed margins, central leaflet with longest stalk. Flowers drooping, in elongated racemes. Corolla 5.5–7 mm long, yellow. Fruit 3–4 mm long, ovate, hairless, with cross furrows.

Flowering season: May–Oct

Habitat: Margins of footpaths and fields, waste ground.

Distribution: Europe; Asia. In BI introduced, mainly in S and C England.

Active ingredients: Coumarin-glycosides, tannins, flavones, mucilage.

Uses: To treat varicose veins, piles. In homeopathy for headaches, migraine, and nose-bleeds (has anti-coagulant properties). Leaf-poultice is antiseptic.

Further uses: Good bee-plant; flowers are source of excellent honey.

47 Kidney Vetch*

Anthyllis vulneraria

(Pea Family)

Hairy plant, to 50 cm tall. Stems simple or branched, rounded, erect. Basal leaves simple, or with few leaflets – large terminal leaflets and smaller laterals. Stem leaves alternate, mostly pinnate; leaflets narrow, with entire margins. Flowers in dense terminal clusters, with 3- to 7-lobed involucre. Calyx whitish or yellowish, woolly and somewhat inflated; weakly 2-lipped. Corolla 1–2 cm long, pale yellow to reddish. Fruit single-seeded, hidden within calyx.

Flowering season: May–Oct

Habitat: Rocks, poor grassland, scrub, mostly on chalk.

Distribution: Europe; E to Caucasus; S to N Africa.

Active ingredients: Saponins, tannins, pigments.

Home use tips: As poultice for wounds, circulation problems and chilblains. Put 2 teaspoonsful in 250 ml boiling water and allow to stand for 15 minutes before use.

48 Rue ✿

Ruta graveolens

(Rue Family)

Perennial to 50 cm tall, with blue-grey foliage, densely covered in aromatic glands, and with strong, distinctive smell. Stems erect, usually branching only in inflorescence. Leaves alternate, stalked, pinnately lobed; leaflets simple or 2- or 3-lobed. Flowers either 4- or 5-partite, in an umbel-like inflorescence. Sepals narrow, oval, falling as fruits ripen. Petals 6–7 mm long, curved, with toothed margins. Fruit a many-seeded, glandular capsule.

Flowering season: June–Aug

Habitat: Rocky slopes, poor grassland, scrub.

Distribution: E Mediterranean; cultivated and naturalised elsewhere in Mediterranean and in parts of C Europe. In BI occasional on waste ground in S.

Active ingredients: Essential oils, coumarin derivatives, alkaloids, rutin (a flavoglycoside).

Uses: To treat varicose and thread veins and some retinal problems. Also for high blood pressure, epilepsy and colic.

Further uses: Leaves have insecticidal properties; sometimes used to flavour food and alcoholic drinks.

NB: Not suitable for collection or home use because coumarin may cause a photo-sensitive adverse skin reaction, and there is a danger of allergic problems caused by the essential oils.

49 Perforate St John's-wort* *Hypericum perforatum*

(St John's-wort Family)

Hairless plant, to 1 m tall with erect, round stem, branching towards top.
Leaves opposite, ovate to linear, with translucent spots. Flowers in clusters.
Sepals 5, narrow, about 6 mm long, with pale or dark glands. Petals 5, elliptic,
10–15 mm long. Stamens numerous; 3–5 styles. Fruit a small capsule.

Flowering season: June–Sep

Habitat: Rocky slopes, dry grassland, meadows, open woods.

Distribution: Europe, except far N; W Asia; N Africa. In BI throughout, but
rare in C and W Scotland.

Active ingredients: Hypericin, essential oils, resins, tannins, flavonoids.

Uses: To treat depression, nervous disorders, bed-wetting, and stomach,
intestinal and gallbladder problems. Externally for healing wounds,
relieving the pain of sprains and bruises, and for rheumatism and lumbago.

Further uses: Leaves for flavouring salads and liqueurs. Flowers yield red
and yellow dyes. Under investigation for possible use in treatment of AIDS.

Home use tips: For depression. Boil 2 teaspoonsful in 250 ml water. Drink
1 cup daily. For external use buy Hypericum oil from the chemist.

NB: Plant can cause dermatitis.

50 Small-leaved Lime* ✿ *Tilia cordata*

(Lime Family)

Deciduous tree to 38 m tall. Relatively short trunk and wide, dense, evenly
domed crown when growing in the open, but a tall, unbranched trunk and high
crown when in closed stands. Bark smooth and thin at first, later dark grey or
blackish, with longitudinal ridges. Shoot finely hairy at first, quickly becoming
smooth and shiny. Leaves alternate, arranged in 2 rows, with 2–5 cm long,
hairless stalk. Blade heart-shaped, 3–10 cm long, pointed, with finely and sharply
toothed margin. Hairless bar vein axils on grey-green lower surface, which have
brownish hairs. Flowers (appearing after the leaves open) yellow-white, strongly
scented, hermaphrodite; in hanging clusters of 3–16. Stalk fused with a pale
green, tongue-shaped bract; perianth 5-partite. Sepals 3 mm long. Petals
yellowish, 3–8 mm. Fruits (Sep) rounded, 5–8 mm across, woody, grey-green,
single-seeded; not obviously ribbed. Fruits fall with the wing-like bract when
ripe.

Flowering season: June–July

Habitat: Mixed broad-leaved woods (oak-hornbeam woods, river-valley
woods). In Britain especially on limestone cliffs. Commonly planted in parks.

Distribution: Europe, W Siberia, Caucasus, Asia. Native in C England
(north to Lake District) and Wales; also planted, and naturalised.

Active ingredients: Essential oil, tannins, mucilage, flavonoids.

Uses: To treat fevers and flu. In homeopathy for rheumatism, hay fever and
allergic skin complaints.

Further uses: As linden tea – aids digestion, improves insomnia. May also
reduce blood pressure and help in cases of arteriosclerosis. Lime water is a
skin tonic. Lime blossom honey is much valued. Bark used to treat gout,
kidney stones and coronary heart disease. Wood yields good charcoal.

Home use tips: Tea (induces sweating in fever). Infuse 1–2 teaspoonsful in
boiling water for 10 minutes. Drink hot, 2–3 cups a day.

Pumpkin/Marrow/Summer Squash

(Cucumber Family)   *Cucurbita pepo*

Annual, with trailing, prickly-hairy stems, to 10 m long. Leaves hairy, alternate, stalked, with heart-shaped base and 5 pointed lobes. Male and female flowers separate on the same plant. Male flowers in groups in leaf axils; female flowers solitary. Calyx bell-shaped, with 5 lobes. Corolla 7–10 cm across, orange-yellow, bell- or funnel-shaped, with 5 distinct lobes. Male flowers have 5 stamens, of which 2 pairs are fused, 1 free. Anthers fused into an S-shape. Female flowers have 3 withered stamens and an inferior ovary. Fruit very variable, depending on cultivar. Round or oval, 15–40 cm across, often yellow, orange or green. Seeds usually whitish, flat and oval, 7–15 mm long.

Flowering season: June–Sep

Habitat: Cultivated in many forms worldwide; occasionally found on rubbish tips, wasteland.

Distribution: Native of Mexico, where it has been in cultivation for at least 8,000 years.

Active ingredients: The amino acid cucurbitin, fatty oil, protein.

Uses: To expel intestinal worms; for bladder and prostate problems. In homeopathy for nausea and vomiting.

Further uses: Flesh eaten in a wide variety of forms: e.g. as vegetable, in soups and jam. Oil yields a culinary oil, used in salads, etc. Roasted seeds eaten as a snack in China, and reputed to promote longevity.

Home use tips: To treat worms eat a handful of pumpkin seeds each day for a fortnight. Alternatively, take a single 30 g dose of pumpkin oil.

Similar species: Marrows, courgettes, custard marrow and the common type of pumpkin all belong to *Cucurbita pepo*. The Giant (Mammoth) Pumpkin and Winter Squashes (including Turban Squash) belong to *C. maxima*, first cultivated in Peru. Buttersquash (and others) (*C. moschata*) comes from C America.

51

52

53 # Wild Pansy/Heartsease* ✿   *Viola tricolor*

(Violet Family)

To 30 cm tall, annual or perennial, with leafy stem. Leaves alternate; lower
leaves rounded with heart-shaped base, with toothed margins, upper leaves
longer, narrowing towards base. Stipules deeply pinnate, with large,
lanceolate terminal lobe. Flowers to 3 cm tall, weakly fragrant. Petals 1.3–2
times as long as calyx, yellow to blue, lower ones with dark stripes; lower lip
yellow. Short spur. Fruit a rounded capsule.

Flowering season: May–Oct

Habitat: Waste ground, fields, meadows.

Distribution: Most of Europe; near east.

Active ingredients: Saponins, flavonoids, salicylates, tannins, mucilage.

Uses: In conventional and homeopathic medicine internally and externally
to treat various skin complaints, respiratory illness and dry coughs.

Home use tips: For skin problems such as acne. Put 2 teaspoonsful in 250
ml boiling water; allow to stand for 10 minutes. Drink 3 cups daily. Can also
be used in a poultice.

Similar species: Field Pansy* (*V. arvensis*). The terminal lobe of the stipule
resembles leaf. Spur about same length as calyx; sepals at least as long as
petals, which are usually pale yellow. Similar habitats and distribution.

54 # Common Evening-primrose* ✿

(Willowherb Family)   *Oenothera biennis*

To about 1 m tall, with downy, leafy stem, somewhat ridged towards top.
Basal leaves lanceolate to obovate, narrowing towards stalk, toothed or with
almost entire margins. Stem leaves many and smaller. Flowers 2–3 cm
long, in leafy racemes, with long, narrow stalk-like tube; opening mainly in
evening. Sepals reflexed. Petals much longer than stamens. Fruits to 3 cm
long, elongated and rectangular.

Flowering season: June–Oct

Habitat: Footpaths, waste ground, dunes, embankments.

Distribution: Europe, except far N. Originally from N America.

Active ingredients: Most notably tannins; fatty acids.

Uses: Formerly to treat diarrhoea.

Further uses: Used by Native Americans as vegetable (leaves and roots).
Roots mixed with honey to make cough syrup. Seeds contain oil good for
skin and to treat eczema. Also for pre-menstrual syndrome.

Note: There are several species of evening-primrose, mostly introduced
from N America.

55 Wild Parsnip*

Pastinaca sativa

(Carrot Family)

Rather hairy plant to 1.5 m tall. Root long and swollen, sometimes beet-shaped, smelling of carrots. Stem erect, branching in upper half. Leaves pinnate, with 2–7 pairs of irregularly toothed lobes. Petals yellow, even-sized, 0.5 mm long, 1 mm wide, curved at outside. Fruit flat and lentil-shaped, 5–7 mm long and 4–5.5 mm wide, narrowly winged, yellow-brown when ripe.

Flowering season: July–Sep

Habitat: Meadows, footpaths, waste ground.

Distribution: Most of Europe; Caucasus; Siberia. Common on chalk in England.

Active ingredients: Essential oil, alkaloids, furocoumarin, fatty oil.

Uses: Earlier for dropsy, stomach and intestinal disorders, and kidney and bladder problems, fever, insomnia, rheumatism.

Further uses: Fruits as spice in soups, salads, stews. Root as vegetable (ancestor of cultivated parsnip, and used by ancient Greeks and Romans).

56 Alexanders*

Smyrnium olusatrum

(Carrot Family)

Hairless, aromatic, to about 1.5 m. Deep green glossy leaves and yellow-green flowers. Leaves shiny green, 3-lobed, with toothed leaflets. Leaf bases with inflated sheaths.

Habitat: Hedges, banks, roadsides and waste ground, usually near the sea. Sometimes around old buildings.

Distribution: NW France southwards. In BI introduced; scattered around coasts, especially Wales, S England and E coast of Ireland. Rare in Scotland.

Flowering season: Apr–June

Active ingredients: Essential oils.

Uses: Juice can be used to clean cuts. Plant aids digestion; roots are mildly diuretic, and leaves rich in vitamin C.

Further uses: Ancient pot-herb, used by Romans in stews and planted as a vegetable in monasteries. Leaves and pickled buds good in salads; cook young stems as asparagus. Flowers can be made into fritters. Root is parsnip flavoured.

57 Lovage* ✿

Levisticum officinale

(Carrot Family)

Hairless, aromatic (rather like Celery) perennial, to 2 m tall. Stems hollow, at base to 5 cm thick, branching towards top. Leaves stalked, large (lower leaves 2- to 3-pinnate and to 70 cm long), with irregularly toothed leaflets. Flowers small, with pale yellow petals, 1 mm long. Fruits compressed, 5–7 mm long.

Flowering season: July–Aug

Habitat: Wasteland, roadsides, abandoned gardens.

Distribution: Native of Iran. Naturalised in Europe. In BI mainly in north.

Active ingredients: Essential oils, resin, bitters, coumarin.

Uses: As diuretic and for bladder and kidney problems, kidney stones. Root used for treating mouth ulcers, bronchitis, cystitis and menstrual pains.

Further uses: Culinary herb; leaves in soups and stews, root grated into salads, seeds on bread or in rice. Used in liqueurs, digestive aperitifs and perfumes.

Home use tips: For stomach ache and digestive upsets. Boil 2 teaspoonsful in 250 ml water. Drink 2 cups daily. **NB: Do not take during pregnancy.**

58 Fennel* ✿ *Foeniculum vulgare*

(Carrot Family)

Hairless, branching perennial with finely cut, feathery leaves, growing to
2 m. Smells of aniseed. Leaves 3- to 4-pinnate, lower leaves stalked, upper
leaves unstalked. Leaves have sheathing bases 3–6 cm long. Flowers in
umbels up to 15 cm across, with 4–25 unequal spokes. Bracts and
bracteoles absent. Petals oval, 0.75–1 mm long. Styles 2, very short. Fruit
oblong, ridged, 4–10 mm long and 2–3 mm wide.

Flowering season: July–Oct

Habitat: Rough, rocky sites; waste land; often near coast.

Distribution: Europe, especially Mediterranean. In BI introduced and
naturalised, mainly in the south.

Active ingredients: Essential oil, fatty oil.

Uses: For coughs, flatulence and other digestive problems.

Further uses: Leaves in salads, young stems in salads and soup, and the
leaves cooked with fish. Fruits used to flavour bread, apple pie, curries and
sauces. Also to flavour liqueurs and toothpaste. Oil sometimes used in
massage. Sweet or Florence Fennel (*F. vulgare* var. *dulce*) has larger, more
aromatic fruits and swollen leaf-bases. It is sliced in salads, or cooked as
vegetable. This form contains the essential oil anethol. Carosella is another
form (*F. vulgare* var. *piperatum*), grown mainly in Italy.

Home use tips: For flatulence and digestive problems. Put 1 teaspoonful
crushed fruits in 250 ml boiling water; leave for 10 minutes. Drink 1 cup,
2–5 times daily. Also suitable for children.

**NB: Use only fruits purchased from reliable stockist or chemist.
Danger of confusion with poisonous species! Do not gather from
the wild.**

59 Dill* ✿ *Anethum graveolens*

(Carrot Family)

Rather like Fennel, but annual. Aromatic plant, to 1 m tall, with thread-like
leaves. Stem erect, hollow and ridged, branching towards the top. Leaves 3-
4-pinnate. Leaves with sheaths to about 2 cm long, encircling stem.
Flowers in rounded umbels to 15 cm across with 30–50 spokes of similar
length (about 8 cm). Bracts and bracteoles absent. Petals bright yellow, to
0.5 mm long and 0.75 mm wide. Styles 2, very short. Fruit oval to circular,
flattened. Individual 'seeds' yellow-brown, winged, with 3 dorsal ridges.

Flowering season: July–Aug

Habitat: Well-drained soils. Planted, occasionally naturalised.

Distribution: W and C Asia. In BI introduced and scattered; casual from
bird seed and grain.

Active ingredients: Essential oil, coumarin derivatives, fatty oil.

Uses: To treat digestive disorders, flatulence and loss of appetite.

Further uses: Oil from seeds is a constituent of gripe water. Culinary herb
for salads, stews and pickles.

Home use tips: For digestive problems and loss of appetite. Put 1
teaspoonful of crushed fruits in 250 ml boiling water; leave for 10 minutes.
Drink 2 cups daily.

58

59

60 Cowslip* ❀ ☒

Primula veris

(Primrose Family)

To 30 cm tall, softly hairy. Leaves in basal rosette, wrinkled, long, ovate, dark green above, pale green beneath, with irregularly notched margin, narrowing abruptly into stalk. Flowers scented, in drooping clusters on a long, leafless stem. Calyx pale green, bell-shaped, inflated, 1–2 cm long, with ovate, pointed teeth. Corolla to 15 mm across, tube-shaped at base, with cup-shaped opening, deep yellow, with orange markings in centre. Fruit a 5–10 mm long, oval capsule.

Flowering season: Apr–May

Habitat: Dry grassland and scrub, roadsides, embankments.

Distribution: Most of Europe; Asia. In BI throughout, but rarer in the north.

Active ingredients: Saponins, flavonoids.

Uses: Expectorant. For coughs and bronchitis.

Further uses: Cowslip wine is a traditional country recipe. However, the species is not as common as it was, so this use should be avoided. Flower tea soothes headaches, and the roots contain aspirin-like compounds.

Home use tips: Tea (treats coughs). 1 teaspoon in 250 ml boiling water; infuse for 5 minutes. Drink 2–3 cups a day, sweetened with honey.

Similar species: Oxlip° ☒ (*P. elatior*) has paler, scentless flowers, lanceolate calyx teeth, wider corolla. Damp meadows and woods, and montane grassland in continental Europe. In Britain a rare flower of certain E Anglian woods.

61 Creeping Jenny* ❀

Lysimachia nummularia

(Primrose Family)

Hairless perennial, to 5 cm tall, with creeping stems up to 50 cm long, freely rooting. Leaves opposite, round to ovate, stalked, often with heart-shaped base, sometimes with red spots (glands). Flowers solitary, in leaf axils; stalk about the same length as leaves. Sepals 5, 7–10 mm long, narrowly heart-shaped and pointed; petals 5, yellow, 9–16 mm long, obovate, with red spots. Stamens much shorter than petals; glandular filaments. Fruit (rarely developed) a rounded capsule, 4–5 mm long.

Flowering season: May–July

Habitat: Damp meadows, gardens, ditches, wet woods, woodland edges.

Distribution: Most of Europe. In Britain, absent from C and N Scotland. In Ireland, mainly in north.

Active ingredients: Saponins, tannins, silicic acid.

Home use tips: Tea (treats coughs). Put 2 teaspoonsful in 250 ml boiling water; infuse for 5 minutes. Drink 3 cups a day, sweetened with honey. Also externally, mixed with the same amount of chamomile tea, use in a bandage to treat slow-healing or festering wounds.

Similar species: Yellow Pimpernel° (*L. nemorum*) has upright stem and oval leaves with translucent spots, flowers in axils of upper leaves, sepals linear, petals lanceolate, unspotted. Yellow flowers with 5 petal-lobes star-shaped and up to 1.2 cm across. Darker yellow spot at the centre of each flower. In damp woods and scrub.

62 Great Yellow Gentian ☒

Gentiana lutea

(Gentian Family)

Hairless plant, to 1.5 m tall, with simple, hollow stem. Leaves to 30 cm long, opposite, elliptic, with strong veins. Flowers in whorls in the upper leaf axils, stalked. Calyx pale yellow, tubular, with 5 teeth, slit along one side. Corolla with short tube, opening into 5–6 narrow, deeply divided lobes. Fruit a round, pointed capsule, to 6 cm long.

Flowering season: July–Aug

Habitat: Tall-herb communities, mountain grassland and scrub.

Distribution: Alps and other mountains of C and SE Europe.

Active ingredients: Bitters (gentiopicrine and amarogentine), pigments, sugar.

Uses: For loss of appetite and digestive disorders.

Further uses: A constituent of gentian bitters (roots and underground stem).

Home use tips: For digestive problems and loss of appetite. Boil 1 teaspoonful in 250 ml water for 5 minutes. Drink 1 warm cup before main meals each day.

63 Spotted Gentian ☒

Gentiana punctata

(Gentian Family)

To 60 cm tall. Flowers sessile; corolla pale yellow with violet spots, bell-shaped, with 5–8 short lobes.

Flowering season: Aug

Habitat: Mountain grassland.

Distribution: C Europe.

Active ingredients, uses and tips: See Great Yellow Gentian.

NB: Both these gentians are protected. Do not collect.

64 Wood Sage*

Teucrium scorodonia

(Mint Family)

Erect, downy plant to 50 cm tall, with rectangular stem, usually branched only towards the top. Leaves opposite, stalked, to 7 cm long, ovate, heart-shaped at base, toothed and wrinkled. Flowers 9–12 mm long, short-stalked, solitary or in pairs in the axils of small bracts. Flowers all tend to bend over to same side of inflorescence. Calyx tubular or bell-shaped, curved and 2-lipped, the upper lip broad, oval and much larger. Corolla pale yellow to greenish-yellow, 9–12 mm long, with projecting tube and down-curved lower lip (lacks obvious upper lip).

Flowering season: June–Oct

Habitat: Open woods, heaths, scrub, wood margins.

Distribution: Most of Europe, except N and E.

Active ingredients: Essential oil, tannins, bitters, flavonoids, anthraquinones.

Uses: In homeopathy for tuberculosis and bronchial catarrh.

Flower

65 # Downy Hemp-nettle* ☒   *Galeopsis segetum*

(Mint Family)

Branching downy annual, to 30 cm tall. Stem not thickened at nodes.
Leaves softly hairy on both sides; stalked, opposite, lanceolate to oval, with
toothed margin, narrowing towards base. Flowers in 1–4 whorl-like clusters
of 4–8. Calyx 0.9–1 cm long, tubular to bell-shaped, 5-lobed. Corolla
2.5–3 cm long, sulphur-yellow, 2-lipped with long tube. Upper lip hooded,
lower lip 3-lobed. Throat yellow or with red-violet marks.

Flowering season: July–Aug

Habitat: Scrub, footpaths, quarries, arable fields.

Distribution: Local in Europe, north to Denmark; east to Hungary and
Romania. In BI native but rare (casual in England and Wales).

Active ingredients: Salicic acid, saponins, tannins, bitters, some essential oil.

Uses: For chronic catarrh. In homeopathy for kidney, bladder and spleen
disorders.

Home use tips: Infusion for coughs. Steep 2 teaspoonsful in 250 ml boiling
water for 10 minutes. Drink 2–3 cups a day, sweetened with honey.

**66
67** # Great Mullein*   *Verbascum thapsus*

(Figwort Family)

To 1.8 m, covered in white, woolly hairs. Leaves long, elliptic, stem leaves
winged along stem down to next leaf, lower leaves stalked. Flowers on short
stalks, grouped together in a dense spike. Calyx woolly. Corolla pale yellow,
with 5 lobes, open funnel-shaped, 18–22 mm across.

Flowering season: July–Sep

Habitat: Woodland margins, clearings, tips.

Distribution: Most of Europe; N Asia.

Active ingredients: Mucilage, saponins, flavonyl-glycosides, some essential
oil.

Uses: Bronchial complaints, coughs. In homeopathy for neuralgia, migraine
and earache.

Further uses: Flowers can reduce eczema and promote healing of wounds;
root extract is diuretic; seed oil for chapped skin.

Home use tips: Infusion for coughs. Steep 2 teaspoonsful of a mixture of
Mullein, Marsh Mallow and Aniseed in 250 ml boiling water for 10
minutes. Drink 2–3 cups a day, sweetened with honey.

Similar species: Orange Mullein* (*V. phlomoides*). Upper leaves not
running far down stem and flowers larger and flatter (30–35 mm across).
Similar habitats. Casual only in Britain.

Note: Contains anti-tubercular substances.

65

66

67

68 Common Toadflax*

Linaria vulgaris

(Figwort Family)

Many-stemmed, hairless perennial, to 90 cm tall with erect, leafy stems.
Leaves mostly alternate, lanceolate to linear, pointed, rather blue-green.
Flowers short-stalked, in dense racemes. Calyx bell-shaped, with 5 pointed
lobes. Corolla pale yellow, 16–30 mm long, 2-lipped, the upper lip with an
orange palate closing entrance; 10 mm long pointed spur at base. Fruit a
capsule, 7–8 mm long, with 4–10 teeth. Seeds disc-shaped, about 2 mm across.
Flowering season: June-Oct
Habitat: Dry grassland, stony slopes, footpaths, waste ground.
Distribution: Most of Europe; W Asia.
Active ingredients: Not well known, includes flavo-glycosides.
Uses: In homeopathy for diarrhoea, inflammation of the large intestine,
bladder problems and bed-wetting.

69 Yellow Foxglove ☒⊛☒

Digitalis grandiflora

(Figwort Family)

Hairy plant, to 1 m tall with upright, unbranched stem. Leaves alternate,
unstalked, long, pointed and irregularly toothed. Flowers short-stalked, in a
spike-like raceme, nodding to one side. Calyx 5-partite, with glandular
hairs. Corolla funnel-shaped, 3–4.5 cm long, pale yellow with brown veins,
inflated, with weakly developed lip.
Flowering season: June–July
Habitat: Woodland edges, scrub, tall-herb communities.
Distribution: C, S and E Europe; east to Siberia. Occasional as garden
escape in BI.
Active ingredients: Cardiac glycosides.
Uses: Occasionally used to treat heart problems.
Similar species: Straw (Small Yellow) Foxglove*, *D. lutea*, occurs in similar
habitats, usually on calcareous soils. It is mainly hairless, corolla 2–2.5 cm long,
pale yellow, with pointed, 2-lobed upper lip. W Europe. In BI introduced,
naturalised and scattered, mainly on waste ground in S England.
NB: Deadly poisonous. Do not collect or use.

70 Grecian Foxglove ☒⊛

Digitalis lanata

(Figwort Family)

To 1 m tall. Leaves narrowly lanceolate, with weakly toothed margins.
Inflorescence with woolly hairs, flowers growing all round, not just to one
side. Flowers stalked; corolla an inflated funnel 2–3 cm long, yellowish with
brownish veins and pale pink lower lip.
Flowering season: June–July
Habitat: Planted as drug crop, and in gardens; waste land.
Distribution: SE Europe. In BI occasional as garden escape.
Active ingredients: Some 60 different cardiac glycosides including digitoxin
and digoxin, saponins, flavonoids.
Uses: To produce a standard drug preparation for serious heart problems.
The cardiac drugs in this species are more potent than those in Common
Foxglove (*D. purpurea*, 142).
NB: Deadly poisonous. Do not collect or use.

71 ## Lady's Bedstraw* *Galium verum*

(Bedstraw Family)

Perennial to 60 cm tall, with rounded, 4-angled stem. Leaves in whorls of
8–12, narrowly linear and with pointed tips, rolled downwards at margins,
about 1 mm across, softly hairy beneath, with a single vein. Flowers small,
numerous, thickly clustered in a much-branched terminal inflorescence.
Calyx absent. Corolla 4-lobed, 2–3 mm across, smelling strongly of honey.

Flowering season: June–Sep

Habitat: Dry grassland, footpaths, roadsides, dunes, open woods.

Distribution: Most of Europe; N Asia.

Active ingredients: Glycosides, tannins, aucubin, flavonoids.

Uses: Externally to prevent bleeding (contains an anti-coagulant).

Further uses: Traditionally as rennet substitute to curdle cheese (one name
of the plant is Cheese-rennet). Double Gloucester and Cheshire were once
made using this plant. The flowers can be made into a drink.

Flower

72 ## Early Goldenrod* ✿ *Solidago gigantea*

(Daisy Family)

Perennial to 2.5 m tall, with hairless lower stem. Leaves alternate,
lanceolate, toothed, hairless below, or with short hairs along veins.
Flowerheads small, erect, in dense clusters on drooping stalks. Ray florets
somewhat longer than involucre and tube florets. Fruit small, with pappus.

Flowering season: Aug–Oct

Habitat: Wet woodland, tall-herb communities, footpaths.

Distribution: N America; garden plant in Europe, including BI; widely
naturalised in BI, but less common than Canadian Goldenrod.

Active ingredients: Alkaloids, saponins, tannins, flavonoids.

Uses: A constituent of many medical preparations, as diuretic.

Similar species: Canadian Goldenrod* ✿ (*S. canadensis*) has thickly hairy
stem and undersides of leaves. Ray florets not longer than involucre and
tube florets. Similar habitats. Introduced.

S. canadensis   S. gigantea
Flowerheads

71

72

73
74
Goldenrod*

Solidago virgaurea

(Daisy Family)

Very variable perennial to 1 m tall, with erect hairless or softly hairy stems, often branching towards top. Leaves alternate. Basal leaves oval or elliptic, coarsely toothed, long-stalked, sparsely hairy or hairless. Stem leaves narrower, entire or toothed, uppermost sessile. Flowerheads 7–18 mm long, 10–15 mm wide, clustered in terminal racemes. Bract scales narrow, lanceolate, with fleshy margins. Ray florets 8–12, longer than involucre and golden yellow, like the tube florets. Fruit with pappus.

Flowering season: July–Oct

Habitat: Poor grassland, clearings, open woods, cliffs, hedgerows.

Distribution: Most of Europe; N Asia; N America.

Active ingredients: Saponins, essential oil, tannins, flavonoids.

Uses: Diuretic, and to treat bladder and kidney problems. Aerial parts are expectorant and anti-inflammatory. A compress can help heal wounds and sores.

Further uses: Flowers and leaves produce a yellow dye.

75
Immortelle ☒

Helichrysum arenarium

(Daisy Family)

Downy perennial to 30 cm tall, with grey, woolly foliage and upright stem, often branching towards top. Leaves alternate; lower leaves narrowly obovate, the upper lanceolate or linear, pointed. Flowerheads round, 6–7 mm across, in groups of 3–20 in dense terminal corymbs. Involucral bracts many and scale-like, yellow or orange, spreading when in fruit. Flowers all tubular, yellow. Fruits 1 mm long, with pappus.

Flowering season: July–Oct

Habitat: Dry grassland, heaths, dunes, footpaths, open pine woods.

Distribution: C and E Europe, north to S Sweden and Denmark; Caucasus.

Active ingredients: Bitters, tannins, essential oil, flavonoids.

Uses: To stimulate digestive juices and strengthen the pancreas. In homeopathy to treat sciatica.

NB: Species declining. Do not collect.

76 Elecampane* ❀ ⊛   *Inula helenium*

(Daisy Family)

Perennial with erect stems, to 1.5 m tall, and a thickened, woody base.
Stems sometimes branching towards top. Leaves alternate and pointed, the
lower ones oval to elliptic, stalked, with undulating margin, sparsely hairy
above and with felty hairs beneath. Upper leaves oval, heart-shaped, sessile
or slightly decurrent. Flowerheads large, 6–7 cm across, solitary or
clustered in loose corymb. Bracts many, scale-like, with large reflexed
appendage at the tip. Ray florets many, long and narrow (1.5 mm wide),
spreading far beyond bracts. Fruits 5 mm long, with pappus.

Flowering season: June–Oct

Habitat: Fields, rough ground.

Distribution: W and C Asia. Naturalised throughout Europe, including BI.
Also planted.

Active ingredients: Essential oil, inulin, bitters.

Uses: Expectorant, for chronic coughs, whooping cough and asthma.

Home use tips: As expectorant. Infuse 1 teaspoon in 250 ml boiling water
for 5 minutes. Drink 1 cup 2–4 times daily, sweetened with honey.

77 Sunflower* ⊛   *Helianthus annuus*

(Daisy Family)

Annual roughly hairy plant to 3 m tall, with thick, erect stem to 10 cm
across. Leaves alternate, stalked, heart-shaped to triangular, pointed, with
toothed margin, with 3 prominent veins and bristly on both surfaces.
Flowerheads very large, to 30 cm across. Bracts fleshy, oval, pointed and
overlapping. Ray florets to 10 cm long and 2 cm wide, golden yellow. Tube
florets brown or greenish-brown. Fruits obovate, laterally flattened,
8–17 mm long and 4–9 mm wide, yellow to deep brown.

Flowering season: Aug–Oct

Habitat: Widely cultivated as crop and ornamental. Casual on waste ground.

Distribution: N America. In Europe (including BI) common casual and
bird-seed alien.

Active ingredients: Flowerheads: flavo-glycosides, anthocyano-glycosides,
xanthophyll, sapogenin. Fruits: oil with unsaturated fatty acids, carotenoids,
lecithin.

Uses: As tincture to treat malaria and tuberculosis. Seeds used as diuretic
and expectorant. Root is a laxative. Oil promotes healing.

Further uses: Yields valuable cooking oil. Seeds eaten raw or cooked; often
added to salads. Also provide food for wild birds in winter.

Home use tips: For aching joints and wounds. Massage with seed-oil or
cover with oil-soaked cloth.

78 Wormwood* ✿

Artenisia absinthium

(Daisy Family)

Silver-grey aromatic perennial, covered in silky hairs, and growing to 1 m
tall. Stem erect, branching with many divided leaves. Leaves alternate;
basal leaves to 25 cm long, stalked, finely divided; stem leaves with shorter
stalks and less divided, upper leaves sessile. Flowerheads 3–4 mm across,
nodding, in much-branched panicle. Scale-like flower bracts of similar
length. Florets all tubular. Fruits 1.5 mm long, without pappus.

Flowering season: July–Sep

Habitat: Waste ground, rocky slopes, footpaths.

Distribution: Europe, Asia, N Africa. Widely naturalised. In BI native,
mainly in England and Wales.

Active ingredients: Essential oil, notably thujon, bitters, absinthin, proazulin.

Uses: For loss of appetite, digestive disorders, liver and gall-bladder
problems. In homeopathy to treat epilepsy, and some other nervous
disorders. Also for treating fever, and to expel worms.

Further uses: As culinary herb or spice. One of original flavourings for
vermouth (the German name of this species is Wermut). Also used in the
liqueur absinthe (now banned). Sometimes grown alongside other plants
for its insecticidal properties.

Home use tips: To stimulate appetite and aid digestion. Infuse 1 teaspoon in
250 ml boiling water for 10 minutes. Drink 3 cups daily, after food.

79
80 Colt's-foot*

Tussilago farfara

(Daisy Family)

Perennial to about 25 cm tall. Flowering stems (centre photo) appearing
before the leaves, unbranched and covered with thick white web-like hairs
and with lanceolate, pointed pinkish scale-like leaves. Flowerheads
terminal, 3–4 cm across; stems with a single row of overlapping scale-like
bracts. Ray florets narrow and spreading, to 14 mm long and bright yellow
in colour. Leaves (bottom photo) large, basal, long-stalked and rounded
with a heart-shaped base. Leaf margins toothed. Upper side of leaf weakly
hairy, underside with a dense covering of white felty hairs.

Flowering season: Mar–Apr

Habitat: Banks, footpaths, damp fields, waste ground.

Distribution: Most of Europe; N Asia; N Africa.

Active ingredients: Mucilage, bitters, tannins, essential oil.

Uses: To treat coughs, sores and ulcers. Flowers reduce inflammation and
ease catarrh.

Further uses: Dried leaves once smoked as remedy for asthma. Flowers
make a good wine. The leaves are rich in vitamin C and can be eaten in salads.

Home use tips: For coughs. Infuse 2 teaspoonsful in 250 ml boiling water
for 10 minutes. Drink 3 cups daily, sweetened with honey.

Similar species: The genus *Petasites* (313/314) is closely related. Members
are easily distinguished by their whitish-pink flowering heads lacking ray
florets. The leaves, although larger, may cause confusion with those of
Colt's-foot. They also appear after the flowers and they sometimes grow in
similar habitats.

78

79

80

81 Arnica ⊠

Arnica montana

(Daisy Family)

Aromatic plant growing to 60 cm with erect, sometimes somewhat
branching stem. Basal leaves ovate or obovate, with 5–7 longitudinal veins,
forming a rosette. Stem leaves (1–2 pairs) opposite, smaller, unstalked.
Flowerheads solitary or in threes (rarely more), terminal, 5–8 cm across.
Bracts in 1–3 rows, lanceolate, pointed. Ray florets narrow, spreading,
2–3 times as long as involucral bracts. Fruits 5 mm long, with pappus.

Flowering season: June–Aug

Habitat: Poor grassland, heaths, dry parts of raised bogs.

Distribution: C Europe north to S Scandinavia; Siberia.

Active ingredients: Essential oil, bitters, procyanidin, flavonoids.

Uses: Externally (though not on broken skin) as antiseptic ointment to
discourage infection in wounds and promote healing, to treat torn muscles
and bruising and for rheumatic problems. Also used as a gargle to treat
inflamed gums and mouth and throat infections. Internally to improve
circulation and treat venous disorders. In homeopathy to treat inflamed
veins, haemorrhage, weak heartbeat, arteriosclerosis and angina. Also used
to treat epilepsy and sea-sickness.

NB: **Protected species. Do not collect.**

82 Pot Marigold/Calendula* ⊛

Calendula officinalis

(Daisy Family)

Hairy plant growing to 50 cm, with characteristic rather unpleasant smell.
Stem erect, usually only branching towards top. Leaves lanceolate or
narrowly obovate; lower leaves stalked, upper leaves unstalked.
Flowerheads solitary and terminal, 2–5 cm across. Flower bracts lanceolate
and pointed, hairy. Ray florets many, 15–20 mm long, twice as long as
bracts. Central florets tubular, but often developing as ray florets in
cultivated forms. Fruits curved. Outer fruits boat-shaped and winged, inner
fruits rolled and circular.

Flowering season: June–Sep

Habitat: Tips and waste ground, old gardens.

Distribution: Long history of cultivation. Possibly of garden origin.

Active ingredients: Essential oil, saponins, bitters, carotenoids, flavonoids.

Uses: Antiseptic and antifungal. Internally to stimulate the liver. In
conventional and homeopathic medicine used externally as a salve to
promote healing on cuts, grazes and spots. Also as a gargle for mouth and
throat infections. Petals yield soothing eyewash.

Further uses: Leaves can be added to salads and flowers to rice and fish.

Home use tips: To treat wounds, abscesses or boils. Infuse 1–2 teaspoonful
for 10 minutes in 250 ml boiling water and put on a bandage.

Tansy* ⊛   *Tanacetum vulgare*

(Daisy Family)

Leafy, aromatic plant growing to 1.2 m tall with a mostly hairless stem,
branched towards the top. Leaves unstalked, pinnately lobed, with long,
sharp-toothed leaflets. Inflorescence an umbel-like head. Individual
flowerheads are tightly-packed, golden yellow and 6–10 mm across, and
give the plant one of its names 'Golden Buttons'. Involucre domed, with
green bract-scales arranged rather like roof tiles. Florets all tube-type, and
extending well beyond bracts.

Flowering season: July–Sep

Habitat: Rough ground, scrub, roadsides, river banks; gardens.

Distribution: Most of Europe; W Asia. Throughout BI, but less common in
Ireland and Scotland.

Uses: In a poultice for rheumatism, varicose veins and bruises. In
homeopathy to expel worms.

Further uses: Flowerheads yield a yellow dye. The leaves contain an
insecticide and can be used to repel flies, ants and fleas, and also mice.

NB: Can be poisonous if taken internally.

Goat's-beard*   *Tragopogon pratensis*

(Daisy Family)

Hairless plant growing to 60 cm with few branches. Stem slightly thickened
below flowerhead, with white latex. Leaves narrowly lanceolate, pointed
and entire, with enlarged base. Flowerheads 18–40 mm across, solitary or
in small groups and with only ray florets. Involucre 25–35 mm long, with
8 linear, pointed bracts. Anthers yellow with black stripes. Fruits
long-stalked, with feathery pappus, forming a large, spherical 'clock'.

Flowering season: May–July

Habitat: Grassland, meadows, embankments, river banks, weedy areas,
waste ground, dunes.

Distribution: Most of Europe.

Uses: Diuretic. Syrup is an expectorant and a petal infusion cleanses the
skin.

Further uses: Roots, shoots and flower buds can be eaten, either cooked, or
raw in salads.

Similar species: T. dubius has stem below inflorescence very much
thickened, and 8–12 bract scales. In dry grassland, mostly on chalk. Not in
British Isles. Salsify° ⊛ (*T. porrifolius*) has purple flowerheads. It is native
to the Mediterranean region, but much cultivated for its edible
white-skinned tap-root. In BI, introduced and casual, mainly in the south.

83

84

85 Dandelion*

Taraxacum officinale

(Daisy Family)

Hairless or sparsely hairy plant to about 50 cm tall, with white latex. Leaves in a basal rosette with very uneven teeth, rarely entire. Flowerheads solitary on a long, leafless stem. Flowerheads with ray florets only. Involucre of small spreading scales on the outside and longer appressed narrow scales on the inside. Fruits with long beaks and umbrella-shaped feathery pappus, forming a spherical 'clock'.

Flowering season: Apr–June (–Dec)

Habitat: Rich meadows, pastures, fields, waste ground.

Distribution: Throughout Europe and W Asia in a wide range of sub-species.

Active ingredients: Bitters, tannins, some essential oils, flavonoids.

Uses: To treat liver and gall-bladder problems. Leaves are diuretic. Also used for treating acne and eczema. Sap used on corns, verrucas and warts.

Further uses: Young leaves good in salads and cooked like spinach. Roots can also be chopped into salads; also used roasted as a coffee substitute. Flowers make a good, slightly resinous wine.

Home use tips: To purify the blood. Put 1–2 teaspoonsful in 250 ml water; bring to the boil for 1 minute. Drink 2 cups daily, for 4–6 weeks.

86 Mouse-ear Hawkweed*

Pilosella officinarum

(Hieracium pilosella)

(Daisy Family)

Variable species growing to about 30 cm tall with single flowerheads on leafless stalks. Leaves linear to obovate, in basal rosettes, with bristles on the upper surface and margins and white, felty hairs below. Rosette sends out leafy runners which can root at the tips. Involucre glandular and hairy. Flowerheads with ray florets only. Fruit with pappus.

Flowering season: May–Oct

Habitat: Dry grassland, heaths.

Distribution: Most of Europe; N Asia; N America.

Active ingredients: Bitters, tannins, umbelliferon, flavonoids.

Uses: To treat (rarely) heart and circulatory disorders.

Home use tips: Internally for mild diarrhoea. Externally as a gargle for mouth or throat infections. Infuse 2 teaspoonsful for 10 minutes in 250 ml boiling water. Drink 2 cups daily, or use as a gargle.

Meadow Saffron (Autumn Crocus)* ☠ ⊗

(Lily Family)   *Colchicum autumnale*

Hairless plant to 25 cm tall with scaly underground corm to 7 cm long.
Leaves all basal, linear-lanceolate and entire, to 40 cm long, with many
parallel veins, appearing with capsule in spring. Flowers singly or in threes,
opening in the Autumn. Flower a long, reddish-purple tube with 6 long
corolla lobes. Stamens 6, shorter than corolla, with orange anthers. Styles 3,
protruding well clear of the corolla tube. Fruit an oval capsule, 3–4 cm
long, opening into 3 valves. Seeds rounded, 0.8–2 mm long, dark brown.
Flowering season: Aug–Sep
Habitat: Damp meadows.
Distribution: Most of Europe. In BI mainly in C England.
Active ingredients: The alkaloid colchicine and related compounds.
Uses: To treat gout, and also leukaemia. In homeopathy for gout,
rheumatism, neuralgia, and for heart and circulatory problems.
**NB: All parts of this species are deadly poisonous. Do not collect or
use.**

Common Bistort* ⊗

(Dock Family)

Persicaria bistorta
(Polygonum bistorta)

Hairless perennial growing to 80 cm tall, with an upright unbranched stem
and widely separated leaves. Leaves ovate with heart-shaped base; to 20 cm
long. Lower leaves with winged stalks, the upper ones stalkless, all with a
stem-enveloping stipule at the base. Inflorescence a dense terminal
cylindrical spike. Flowers 5-lobed, pink to red in colour and 4–5 mm long.
Fruit a 4–5 mm dark brown shiny triangular nut.
Flowering season: May–July
Habitat: Damp meadows, open woodland, roadsides.
Distribution: W and C Europe, S Europe only in mountains; N Asia;
N America. Rare in Ireland. In Britain commonest in NW England.
Active ingredients: Tannins (large amounts), starch, protein, traces of
anthraquiinone.
Uses: The Latin name 'bistorta' (meaning twice-twisted) refers to the shape
of the rootstock. This species was quoted in 16th century herbals as
Snakeroot, and extracts from the roots were used to treat snake bites.
Previously the rootstock was held by apothecaries under the name of 'Radix
Bistortae'. It is used as an internal medicine to treat diarrhoea, and
externally for infections of the mouth and throat.
Further uses: Young shoots and leaves can be eaten as a vegetable, as can
roasted roots. An ingredient of Easter-ledge pudding in the Lake District.
Home use tips: As a gargle for mouth or throat infections or as poultice for
infected wounds. Put 2 teaspoonsful in 250 ml of luke-warm water; leave to
stand for 5 hours before use.

90 Soapwort* ✿ ⊛

Saponaria officinalis

(Pink Family)

Mainly hairless perennial growing to 70 cm tall with upright stem. Leaves lanceolate and opposite, 3-veined, stalkless. Flowers weakly scented, clustered in axils of upper leaves, often 'doubled'. Calyx tube-shaped, 17–20 mm long, with 5 teeth. Petals 5, 30–40 mm long, pale pink or white. Fruit a single-celled capsule. Seeds blackish, round or kidney-shaped, 1.8 mm long.

Flowering season: June–Sep

Habitat: Footpaths, waste ground, river banks, old gardens.

Distribution: Europe; W Asia. Scattered through BI (probably introduced), often near old gardens (an ancient cultivated herb).

Active ingredients: Saponins.

Uses: Expectorant, for bronchial catarrh. Produces a gentle wash for the skin (good for acne and eczema).

Further uses: Flowers can be added to salads.

91 Summer Pheasant's-eye ⊛🗙

Adonis aestivalis

(Buttercup Family)

Hairless plant to 40 cm tall with dense covering of unstalked feathery pinnate leaves. Flowers solitary and terminal, 1–3.5 cm across. Sepals 5, green and hairless. Petals 5–8, rather long. Stamens many. Fruits (achenes) keeled on upper side, mostly with 2 teeth and a short, straight beak at the tip.

Flowering season: May–July

Habitat: Agricultural fields; mostly on calcareous soils.

Distribution: S Europe; Asia. Not in BI.

Active ingredients: Cardiac glycoside adonine.

Uses: Used formerly for heart problems.

Similar species: Large Pheasant's-eye (*A. flammea*) has stem softly hairy at base, hairy sepals, and fruits with obvious tooth on the underside and twisted beak. Pheasant's-eye° (*A. annua*) is a similar species which occurs rarely as an arable weed in S England.

92 Common Fumitory* ☠

Fumaria officinalis

(Fumitory Family)

Hairless annual growing to 30 cm tall. Stems weak, upright, branched. Leaves stalked, twice-pinnate, blue-green and feathery. Tips of leaflets 3–4 times as long as wide. Inflorescence a raceme with 10–50 flowers, in leaf axils. Sepals 2, toothed, on sides of flower. Corolla pink with dark tip, 6–9 mm long, 2-lipped, with a rather short, thick spur. Fruit a rounded achene, 2-3 mm across.

Flowering season: Apr–Oct

Habitat: Arable fields, waste ground, roadsides.

Distribution: Europe; W Asia; N Africa.

Active ingredients: Alkaloids, fumaric acid, bitters, flavonoids.

Uses: To treat gall-bladder complaints. Also internally as a cleansing agent and as diuretic and laxative. Externally as antiseptic lotion.

Similar species: Few-flowered Fumitory° (*F. vaillantii*). Leaf tips 4–6 times as long as wide. Sepals 0.5–1 mm long, pale pink. Fruit rounded, with small point at end. Fruit-stalk scarcely longer than bract. Similar habitats.

NB: Caution. Can be poisonous in large doses.

Common Poppy* ✽

Papaver rhoeas

(Poppy Family)

Hairy annual to 70 cm tall with upright stem, feathery leaves and toothed leaflets. Flowers to 8 cm across, solitary and terminal, drooping in bud, becoming erect in flower. Sepals 2, green, with bristly hairs; falling early. Petals 4, scarlet, about 4 cm long, often each with black spot towards the base. Stamens numerous. Fruit a rounded capsule with 8–18 rays on stigma.

Flowering season: May–July

Habitat: Arable fields, waste ground, edges of footpaths.

Distribution: Virtually worldwide.

Active ingredients: Alkaloids, notably rhoeadine, anthocyano-glycosides, mucilage.

Uses: Occasionally as expectorant to treat coughs. Also to colour medicines.

Further uses: Seeds yield oil and also used in baking.

Similar Species: Long-headed Poppy* (*P. dubium*, 94). Petals 1–2 cm long, fruit longer and narrower, with 6–9 rayed stigma. Similar habitats.

P. rhoeas   P. dubium
Capsules

Opium Poppy* ☠ ✽

Papaver somniferum

(Poppy Family)

Sturdy, usually hairless annual with bluish-green foliage, growing to 1.5 m. Stem simple or branched. Whole plant contains milky sap. Leaves oval, with undulate or toothed margin; lower leaves stalked, upper leaves sessile and clasping. Flowers to 10 cm across. Sepals 2, green; falling early. Petals 4, pale pink or pale violet, more rarely white, each with dark spot at base. Stamens numerous. Fruit an almost spherical capsule, up to 9 cm long, with 5–12 rays on stigma. Seeds 0.9–1.6 mm long, brownish-violet.

Flowering season: June–Aug

Habitat: Waste ground, cultivated areas.

Distribution: SE Europe, W Asia. Long cultivated and naturalised elsewhere. In BI common as casual.

Active ingredients: The sap contains at least 30 alkaloids, notably morphine, codeine, papaverine, and thebaine. Mucilage. The dried sap from the unripe fruit capsules of one form (ssp. *somniferum*) is the drug opium, which can be purified into the more dangerous heroin.

Uses: Opium and derivatives are widely used in medicine, for example in severe diarrhoea and to calm the intestine after operations. Morphine is a powerful painkiller and codeine helps soothe violent coughing. Papaverine is used to treat stomach cramps and some urinary and gall-bladder complaints.

Further uses: Seeds of ssp. *hortense* added to bread, curries and some other foods.

NB: Preparation of drugs is strictly illegal.

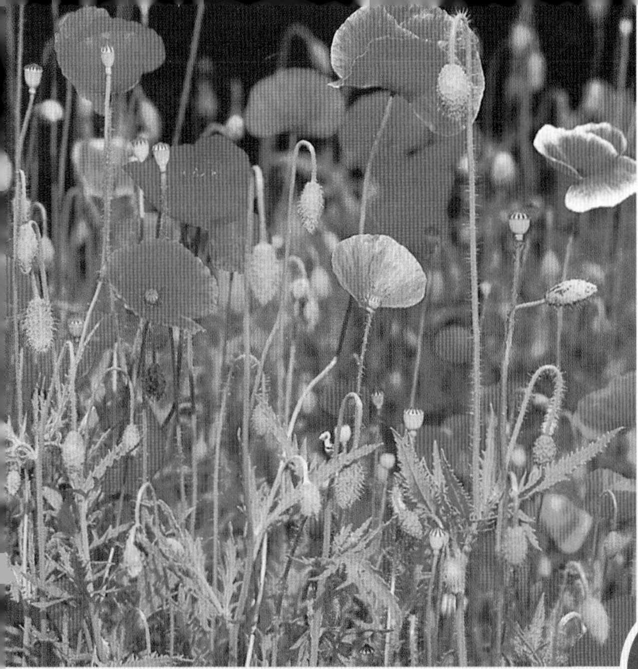

93

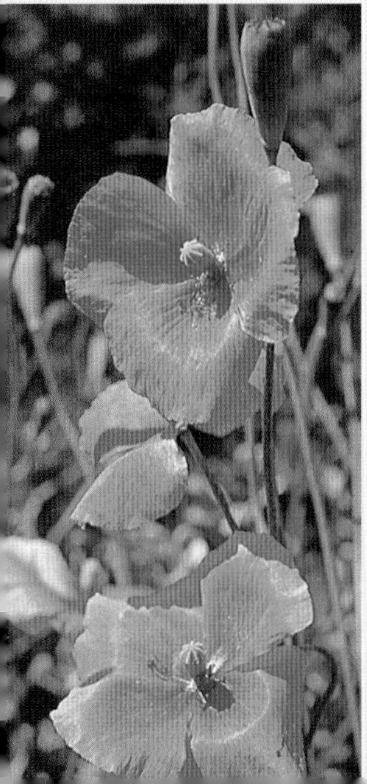

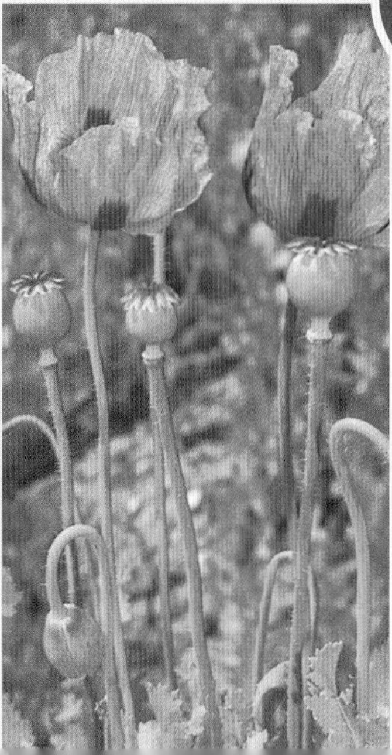

94

95

Cuckooflower/Lady's Smock*

(Cabbage Family)   *Cardamine pratensis*

Almost hairless perennial to 30 cm tall, with a rosette of stalked, pinnate basal leaves each with up to 14 rounded lateral leaflets. Terminal leaflet is the largest, to 1.5 cm across. Stem leaves stalkless, with narrow, linear leaflets. Flowers 4-partite, to 1 cm across. Sepals 2.8–4 mm long. Petals 8–13 mm long, pale pink or white. Fruit 2–4 cm long, 1–1.5 mm wide.

Flowering season: May–July

Habitat: Damp meadows, scrub, wet woodland.

Distribution: Most of Europe; Asia; N America.

Active ingredients: Mustard-oil glycosides, vitamin C.

Uses: In homeopathy to treat stomach cramps.

Further uses: Leaves can be used in salads, stews and soups, and cooked as a vegetable.

Similar species: Hairy Bitter-cress° (*C. hirsuta*) has leaflets hairy on upper surface, and white flowers 3–4 mm across. Waste or rocky ground.

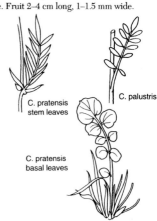

C. pratensis stem leaves

C. palustris

C. pratensis basal leaves

Dog-rose*

(Rose Family)   *Rosa canina*

Variable woody perennial with thorny twigs. Thorns strongly down-curved. Leaves compound, with 5–7 irregularly toothed leaflets. Stipules long, narrow and with glandular hairs. Flowers, 4–5 cm across, solitary or in small groups. Sepals curving back after flowering and falling off before fruit ripens. Outer sepals with narrow, projecting side-lobes. Petals 5, pink, occasionally white. Stamens many. Styles many, stigmas forming a small head. Fruit oval, 1.5 cm long, fleshy, red.

Flowering season: May–June

Habitat: Hedgerows, wood margins, rocky slopes.

Distribution: Europe; N Africa; W and N Asia. In BI absent from much of the north.

Active ingredients: Tannins, fruit acids, carotenoids, rutin, vitamin C (especially in the fruits).

Uses: As diuretic, to treat kidney and bladder stones. Rose-water good for tired eyes.

Further uses: Fruits (hips) for making jam, juice and tea; also soup. Petals can be crystallised for cake decoration or dried in pot-pourris. Oil used in many perfumes.

Home use tips: A tea to aid recovery after cold or fever. Boil 2 teaspoonsful of rose-hips in 250 ml water for 10 minutes.

96

Great Burnet*   *Sanguisorba officinalis*

(Rose Family)

Plant to 90 cm tall with mostly leafless upper stem. Leaves pinnate, with roughly-toothed leaflets. Basal leaves in a rosette. Stem leaves alternate, smaller. Flowers brownish-red, small, lacking petals, in tight, oval inflorescences. Calyx 4-partite. Stamens 4. Fruit a small, ridged achene.

Flowering season: June–Sep

Habitat: Damp meadows, ditches, footpaths.

Distribution: Most of Europe; Caucasus, Asia. In Britain mainly C and N England. Absent from most of Scotland and rare in Ireland.

Active ingredients: Tannins, saponins, flavonoids, vitamin C.

Uses: In homeopathy for treating varicose veins and irregular periods.

Similar species: Salad Burnet* (*S. minor*) has pinnate basal leaves, reddish stems and dense, round flowerheads. Fresh leaves are good in salads.

Note: The generic name comes from sanguis (blood) and sorbere (to absorb), referring to the plant's ability to reduce bleeding.

Red Clover*   *Trifolium pratense*

(Pea Family)

Variable, hairy perennial with leafy, branching stem, growing to around 60 cm. Leaf a large typical clover leaf with 3 obovate to elliptic leaflets, often each with a pale white semicircular marking above. The flowerheads are rounded and pink, to 1.5 cm long, encircled by upper leaves. Calyx tube-shaped, with 10 veins. Corolla 1.3–1.8 cm long. Fruit a small pod, mostly hidden in calyx.

Flowering season: May–Oct

Habitat: Grassy banks, roadsides, meadows, waste ground.

Distribution: Europe; Asia; N Africa; America.

Active ingredients: Tannins, glycosides, phenols.

Uses: Earlier used to treat coughs. Recent research has revealed anti-coagulant and anti-tumour activity.

Further uses: Flowers and leaves can be cooked as vegetable, or used in salads.

Home use tips: For coughs. Infuse 4–6 dried flowerheads in 250 ml boiling water; stand for 15 minutes. Drink 2–3 cups daily, sweetened with honey.

Hare's-foot Clover*   *Trifolium arvense*

(Pea Family)

Grey, hairy annual or biennial to 40 cm tall, with erect, branching stem. Leaves alternate, trifoliate, with narrow leaflets. Inflorescence a long oval shape, 1–3 cm, 1 cm wide, stalked, with woolly hairs. Calyx 10-veined, with 5 feathery teeth. Corolla 3–4 mm long, shorter than the calyx, white first, later pink.

Flowering season: May–Aug

Habitat: Footpath edges, arable fields, open grassland, heaths.

Distribution: Most of Europe; spread almost worldwide. Locally common, and often coastal in Britain. Absent from much of Scotland and Ireland.

Active ingredients: Tannins, essential oil, resin.

Uses: In homeopathy for diarrhoea, chronic gastritis and arthritis.

Home use tips: For diarrhoea. Boil 2 teaspoonful in 250 ml water and stand for 1–2 minutes. Drink 3 times daily, unsweetened.

102 Spiny Restharrow*

Ononis spinosa

(Pea Family)

Shrubby perennial to 50 cm tall with 1 or 2 rows of glandular hairs on stem, and usually paired thorns in leaf axils. Lower leaves with 3 narrow, toothed leaflets; upper leaves often entire. Flowers pink, short-stalked, usually solitary, in the axils of the upper stem leaves. Corolla 1–2.5 cm long. Pods oval, as long as or longer than calyx.

Flowering season: July–Oct

Habitat: Dry grassland, wasteland, footpath edges.

Distribution: C and W Europe northwards to S Scandinavia and Britain. Rare in Scotland; absent from Ireland.

Active ingredients: Essential oils, flavonoid-glycosides, tannins.

Uses: To treat bladder and kidney problems, and water retention.

Similar species: Common Restharrow° (*O. repens*) is more prostrate, has stems hairy all round, and lacks strong spines. Pod shorter than calyx.

103 Herb-Robert*

Geranium robertianum

(Crane's-bill Family)

Rather a spreading annual or biennial to 50 cm tall, with a strong smell and hairy stems and leaves. Stem rather fragile, branching, with thickened nodes and often tinged red. Leaves opposite and stalked, with 3–5 deeply cut lobes. Flowers mostly in pairs, short-stalked. Flower stalks and calyx with glandular and non-glandular hairs. Sepals 6–8 mm long, erect, pointed. Petals 9–12 mm long, rounded. Anthers orange. Fruit 0.5–1.5 cm long.

Flowering season: May–Oct

Habitat: Woods, scrub, clearings, walls; attractive garden 'weed'.

Distribution: Europe; most of Asia; N America; N Africa.

Active ingredients: Tannins, bitters, essential oil.

Uses: In homeopathy to treat internal bleeding. Also a diuretic and once used for toothache. Mouth antiseptic.

Home use tips: As a gargle for mouth and gum infections, and to clean bleeding wounds. Infuse 2 teaspoonsful in 250 ml boiling water for 5 minutes.

104 (Garden) Nasturtium* ⊛   *Tropaeolum majus*

(Nasturtium Family)

Annual, with hairless, trailing, succulent stems. Grows up to 5 m long, using leaf stalks to clamber, and occasionally rooting at nodes. Leaves almost circular, with undulate margin, 3–5 cm across and centrally placed stalk. Flowers long-stalked and zygomorphic, solitary in leaf axils, with a spur to 2.8 cm long. Sepals 5, somewhat unequal. Petals 5, yellow, red or orange. Fruit of 3 single-seeded sections.

Flowering season: Capable of flowering most of year (given right conditions).

Habitat: Well-drained soils. Gardens, waste ground, tips.

Distribution: Peru. Introduced. Frequent casual.

Active ingredients: Mustard-oil glycosides, glucotropaeolin.

Uses: For bronchitis, infections of respiratory and urinary tracts, and kidney.

Further uses: Pickled buds used like capers. Leaves and flowers can be added to salads and other foods. Reputed to have aphrodisiac qualities.

Home use tips: Add small amounts of fresh leaves to spring salads (purifies the blood).

105 Burning Bush ⊛ ☒   *Dictamnus albus*

(Rue Family)

Tall hairy plant to 1.2 m, smelling of cinnamon and covered with black glands, especially towards the top. Leaves stalked, pinnate, with 7–11 finely-toothed oval leaflets. Flowers clustered in a terminal raceme. Each flower weakly zygomorphic, to 5 cm broad, 5-partite. Sepals 6–28 mm long. Petals 2–3 cm long, pink with dark veins, 4 petals growing upwards, the lower petal curved downwards. Stamens 10, curving upwards. Fruit 1 cm long, 5-partite.

Flowering season: May–June

Habitat: Dry slopes, open woodland, scrub.

Distribution: C and S Europe; Asia. A garden plant only in BI.

Active ingredients: Alkaloids, saponins, bitters, essential oils, flavo-glycosides.

Uses: In homeopathy for stomach and intestinal disorders, flatulence, and for irregular or painful periods.

NB: Protected species. Do not collect.

Note: Like all members of the Rutaceae (such as *Citrus* fruits) this species contains many essential oils, which are given off in such quantities on hot days that they fill the air surrounding the plants. These oils protect the plants from desiccation and are flammable (hence common name).

106 Marsh Mallow*

Althaea officinalis

(Mallow Family)

Softly hairy perennial to 1.5 m tall with upright stem. Leaves alternate, short-stalked, grey-green, thick and covered in silky hairs. Lower leaves triangular or heart-shaped, toothed or weakly 3–5 lobed. Upper leaves oval, toothed. Flowers, each up to 5 cm across, in small groups in the axils of upper leaves. Calyx 5-partite. Epicalyx 8–10 partite. Petals broad and heart-shaped, pale pink, bearded towards the base. Fruit ring-shaped and hairy, at the base of the calyx.

Flowering season: July–Sep

Habitat: Damp meadows, banks, particularly near the sea.

Distribution: C and E Europe, north to Britain and Denmark. N Asia.

Active ingredients: Mucilage, sugar, pectin, essential oil (leaves).

Uses: To treat mouth and throat infections and gastric ulcers. Roots and leaves can be used as a poultice.

Further uses: Flowers and young leaves can be added to salads. Leaves and roots can be eaten as vegetables (latter boiled and fried). In cosmetics for the skin. The roots were once used as sweets (the original marshmallows).

Home use tips: As gargle for mouth or throat infections. Leave 2 teaspoonful to stand in 250 ml cold water for half an hour. Drink 1–3 cups (warmed up) daily, or use as a gargle.

107 Hollyhock* ⊗

Alcea rosea

(Mallow Family)

Tall biennial or perennial with stiff stems reaching 3 m. Leaves long-stalked and wrinkled, 5–9 lobed. Flowers in groups of 1–4, in upper leaf axils, and each 6–10 cm across. Sepals 5. Epicalyx shorter than calyx and 6–9 partite, with fused base. Petals red to dark purple, yellow or white, bearded at base. Fruit breaking into nutlets.

Flowering season: July–Sep

Habitat: Gardens, waste ground, tips.

Distribution: W Asia. Common garden plant. Casual garden escape in BI.

Active ingredients: Mucilage, anthocyanins, tannins.

Uses: Infusion as gargle. Flowers yield a dye.

108 Common Mallow*

Malva sylvestris

(Mallow Family)

Robust, hairy perennial, to 1.2 m tall, with branching stem. Leaves stalked, with 3–7 ovate, toothed lobes. Flowers in groups in the leaf axils. Sepals 5, fused to mid-point. Epicalyx with 2–3 lobes. Petals 2–3 cm long, notched, pink or purple with dark veins. Fruit a ring of nutlets about 1 cm across. The individual nutlets have irregular wrinkles along the back, and indistinct radial stripes at the side.

Flowering season: May–Sep

Habitat: Footpaths, waste ground, roadsides, fields.

Distribution: Virtually worldwide.

Active ingredients: Mucilage, anthocyanins, tannins.

Uses: For coughs and throat infections, and stomach and intestinal irritations.

Further uses: Makes good soup (use young leaves).

Mezereon* ☠ ⊗ ☒   *Daphne mezereum*

(Mezereon Family)

Deciduous shrub, to 1.5 m tall. Young shoots hairy and with leaves only towards the tips. Leaves short-stalked, to 8 cm long by 2 cm wide, hairless or with soft hairs at margin. The fragrant pink flowers (top) grow in cylindrical clusters in axils of previous year's fallen leaves and usually open before the new leaves. Flower 4–10 mm long with 4 petaloid sepals. True petals absent. Fruit (centre left) an oval, scarlet berry (technically a drupe).

Flowering season: Feb–Apr

Habitat: Shady woods, scrub; calcareous soils.

Distribution: Most of Europe; Siberia; Turkey; Caucasus. Rare as a native in Britain.

Active ingredients: Coumarin-glycoside, daphnine, resin, daphnetoxin, flavonoids.

Uses: In homeopathy for various skin complaints, eczema, rashes and shingles.

NB: This plant is both poisonous and protected. Do not collect or use.

Pomegranate   *Punica granatum*

(Pomegranate Family)

Shrub or small tree to 5 m tall. Twigs winged when young, ridged and sometimes bearing thorns. Leaves mostly opposite, oval or lanceolate, hairless and short-stalked; often in bushy arrangement. Flowers (centre right) in small groups (1–3) at shoot tips, each 4–6 cm across. Calyx bright orange-red, with 5–9 triangular teeth. Petals red, 5–8, delicate, often crinkly, 2–3 cm long. Stamens about 20, curved inwards. Fruit (below) apple-like, to 12 cm across, with leathery skin and persistent sepals at the top. Inside there are 2 layers: the top layer with 3 chambers; the lower with 6–9 chambers. The seeds are each embedded in translucent edible pulp.

Flowering season: June–Oct

Habitat: Scrub, maquis. Widely grown and naturalised.

Distribution: Native of Afghanistan and Pakistan; widely planted, especially in Mediterranean region.

Active ingredients: Alkaloids and tannins (mainly from bark).

Uses: In homeopathy to treat dizziness. Rind used against dysentery, and root bark against tapeworm.

Further uses: The fruit is tasty and refreshing. Juice used to flavour drinks, including grenadine. Fruits also a constituent of Middle Eastern cuisine. Fruit and bark also yield dyes.

109
110
111
112

113 Umbellate Wintergreen ☒ *Chimaphila umbellata*

(Wintergreen Family)

Perennial shrubby hairless plant to 25 cm tall. Stem ridged and woody at base. Leaves dark green, short-stalked, leathery, evergreen, lanceolate, and toothed in upper half. Inflorescence a 2–7 flowered umbel-like cluster, to 10 cm tall. Flowers stalked and nodding, 10–12 mm across. Sepals rounded and toothed. Petals 5, pale pink, oval and curved. Stamens 10, with red anthers. Style very short; stigma flat. Fruit a furrowed capsule, 5–6 mm long.

Flowering season: June–July

Habitat: Dry, sandy pinewoods.

Distribution: C, N and E Europe; N Asia to Japan; N America.

Active ingredients: Arbutin (hydroquinone-glycoside), chimaphilin, tannins.

Uses: In homeopathy to treat chronic bladder infections and pyelitis, and for prostate problems.

NB: Plant protected. Do not collect.

114 Heather* ⊛ *Calluna vulgaris*

(Heather Family)

Shrub up to 1 m tall with much-branched stem. Leaves evergreen, scale-like, arranged in fours and overlapping each other rather like roof tiles, each 1–3.5 mm long and unstalked. Flowers clustered along one side of stem in dense racemes. 4-lobed green epicalyx surrounds base of each flower. Sepals 4, pink and oval, 4 mm long, forming bell-shaped calyx. Petals only half as long as calyx and fused towards base. Stamens 8, anthers with 2 outcurved horns at tip. Fruit a small capsule with tiny seeds.

Flowering season: July–Nov

Habitat: Heaths, moorland, pinewoods, dunes; poor soils.

Distribution: Europe; W Siberia; N America (introduced).

Active ingredients: Arbutin (hydroquinone-glycoside), hydroquinone, tannins, flavone-glycosides.

Uses: Flowers are antiseptic, astringent, diuretic and sedative. To treat urinary infections. Heather extract used to treat rheumatism and eczema.

Further uses: Twigs used for brooms ('kalluno' means 'to brush' in Greek). Dried flowers for tea; shoots to flavour beer. Flowers produce a good honey, and also yield a dye.

Home use tips: As diuretic for bladder and kidney problems; externally as a wash for eczema. Put 1–2 teaspoonsful in 250 ml boiling water. Leave to stand for 10 minutes. Drink 2–3 cups a day, lukewarm.

113

114

Bilberry*

Vaccinium myrtillus

(Heather Family)

Deciduous hairless, branching shrub to 50 cm tall, with green, winged stem. Leaves oval, pointed, very short-stalked and with finely-toothed margin. Flowers (top left) are solitary in leaf axils, drooping, 4–7 mm long, urn-shaped and pale green or pink. Calyx with 5 short lobes. Anthers yellow-brown, with 2 upwardly projecting horns. Fruit (top right) a dark blue rounded berry, 5–8 mm across.

Flowering season: May–June

Habitat: Heather moors, shady, acid woods.

Distribution: C and N Europe (in S Europe restricted to mountains); N Asia; N America. Throughout BI, but rare in E Anglia and Midlands.

Active ingredients: Tannins, vitamins, fruit acids, flavones.

Uses: To support treatment of diabetes. Also used for diarrhoea.

Further uses: Berries used to make jam and in puddings and pies.

Home use tips: To treat diarrhoea, especially in small children. Boil 3 dessert spoonsful of dried berries in 250 ml water for 10 minutes. Drink half a cup 2–3 times a day.

Bog Bilberry* ☠

Vaccinium uliginosum

(Heather Family)

Deciduous shrub to 80 cm tall, with entire, blue-green thin leaves with obvious veins on underside. Flowers in small clusters at the ends of shoots. Corolla short, 4–6 mm long, urn-shaped and drooping, 4- to 5-partite, white to pink. Calyx short. Fruit a dark blue berry 7–10 mm across.

Flowering season: May–June

Habitat: Bogs and heaths, moorland, coniferous woodland, subalpine scrub.

Distribution: C and N Europe; N Asia; N America. Absent from Ireland. In Britain mainly in Scotland and N England.

Active ingredients: Arbutin, flavone-glycosides.

Uses: Fruits edible, and can be made into jam.

NB: Plant (apart from fruits) somewhat poisonous.

Scarlet Pimpernel* ☠

Anagallis arvensis

(Primrose Family)

Hairless annual to 10 cm tall, with straggling rectangular stems. Leaves opposite, to 2 cm long, oval to lanceolate, pointed and stalkless. Flowers in the leaf axils, solitary, long-stalked and 5-partite. Sepals 4–5 mm long, joined together at the base. Corolla 5–7 mm long, divided almost to the base, usually red, sometimes blue and rarely pink. Corolla lobes widely spread, entire, with glandular hairs at the edges. Fruit a 4–5 mm long lidded capsule, opening around the middle.

Flowering season: June–Oct

Habitat: Cultivated land, waste ground, dunes.

Distribution: Almost worldwide.

Active ingredients: Saponins, tannins, flavonoids.

Uses: In homeopathy to treat rashes, and liver and gallbladder problems.

NB: Poisonous. Do not use.

119 Purple Gentian ✿ ☒

Gentiana purpurea

(Gentian Family)

Erect, hairless perennial, to 60 cm tall, with sturdy rootstock and hollow
stem. Leaves opposite, narrowly ovate, with 5 veins. Lower leaves stalked,
upper leaves sessile. Flowers in terminal clusters of 5–10 and a few in lower
whorls, in upper leaf axils. Calyx bell-shaped and 2-lobed, split almost to
the base on one side. Corolla up to 3.5 cm long, trumpet-shaped, with 5–8
short lobes at the top. Red or dull purple outside, yellowish inside. Anthers
fused to form tube. Fruit an elongated capsule.

Flowering season: July–Sep

Habitat: Mountain pasture, tall-herb communities, mountain woodland.

Distribution: Local in W Alps, Apennines, S Norway.

Active ingredients: The glycosides gentiopicrin and amarogentin.

Uses: In conventional and homeopathic medicine for digestive disorders,
loss of appetite, flatulence, and to stimulate digestive secretions. Also for
liver and gall-bladder problems.

Further uses: A constituent of gentian schnapps.

NB: All gentian species are protected. Do not collect.

120 Common Centaury* ☒

Centaurium erythraea

(Gentian Family)

Hairless biennial to 30 cm tall, with stem branching towards the top. Lower
leaves narrowly oval, growing in a rosette. Stem leaves unstalked, opposite,
oval and pointed. Flowers pink, in a loose, branched, flat-topped
inflorescence. Calyx half the length of corolla tube, with pointed teeth.
Corolla tubular, 10–15 mm long, opening out into a star-shaped flower
about 15 mm across. Fruit a cylindrical capsule, 7–10 mm long.

Flowering season: July–Sep

Habitat: Meadows, clearings, dry slopes.

Distribution: Europe; Asia; N Africa. Common throughout BI, except
Scotland, where local and mostly coastal.

Active ingredients: Gentiopicrin and amarogentin.

Uses: For digestive disorders, loss of appetite, and to stimulate digestive
secretions. Also for liver and gallbladder problems.

Further uses: A constituent of digestive bitters.

Home use tips: For flatulence and to stimulate digestive juices. Infuse
1 teaspoonful in 250 ml cold water for 6–10 hours. Take 1 cup (warmed)
before each meal.

**NB: Protected species. Do not collect. Use only commercial
preparations.**

119

120

Oleander ☠☒

Nerium oleander

(Oleander Family)

Hairless, evergreen shrub, growing to 5 m tall. Leaves mainly in whorls of 3, leathery, lanceolate and pointed, narrowing into a short stalk, with obvious midrib and many almost parallel veins. Flowers pink, red or white, in terminal clusters. Calyx deeply 5-lobed, glandular. Corolla with short tube, opening into 5 lobes, each with slight twist to the right and with toothed scale-like appendages at the throat. Stamens enclosed within tube. Fruit a large follicle, 2–15 cm long, splitting open when ripe.

Flowering season: Apr–Sep

Habitat: River banks, dry river beds close to groundwater. Often grown in gardens, parks and alongside roads.

Distribution: Mediterranean region.

Active ingredients: Cardiac glycosides, flavone-glycosides.

Uses: Standard preparation used to treat certain heart complaints. In homeopathy also for cardiac conditions and angina; intestinal problems; also for eczema and cradle-cap.

NB: Very poisonous. Do not collect or use.

Common Comfrey*

Symphytum officinale

(Borage Family)

Thickly hairy plant to 1.5 m tall. Stem angled and winged, unbranched or branching only towards the top. Leaves lanceolate; lower ones stalked and up to 25 cm long, the upper ones shorter and unstalked. The wings of the leaves project downwards along the stem as far as the next leaf. Inflorescences in axils of upper leaves, dense, hanging over to one side. Calyx 5-lobed almost to base. Flowers purplish-violet, pink, or creamy-yellow. Corolla 1.2–2 cm long, fused and tubular, with 5 small scales in the throat between the 5 stamens. Style projecting beyond corolla.

Flowering season: May–July

Habitat: Damp meadows, river banks, marshes, fens.

Distribution: Europe; Asia.

Active ingredients: Allantoin, tannins, mucilage, pyrrolizidine-alkaloids, calcium, potassium and phosphorus.

Uses: In homeopathy for fractures, bruises, painful joints and circulatory problems. Leaf tea used for coughs and digestive ulcers, and a poultice for sprains, burns, sores, cuts, and eczema.

Further uses: Young leaves can be cooked and used as a spinach-like vegetable.

Home use tips: As poultice. Boil 100 g root in 1 l water for 10 minutes.

Similar species: The introduced hybrid Russian Comfrey* (*S.* x *uplandicum*) is commoner in BI than Common Comfrey, particularly on roadsides and rough ground. It is more bristly, and has blue, violet or purple flowers.

NB: Internal use not recommended, as plant may have some carcinogenic effect. Nevertheless, Comfrey is also being investigated for possible anti-tumour activity.

121

122

123
124

Hound's-tongue*

Cynoglossum officinale

(Borage Family)

Softly hairy, much-branched leafy biennial with grey-green foliage, growing to 80 cm tall. Leaves lanceolate, up to 20 cm long, entire; lower leaves tapering gradually into a winged stalk, upper leaves sessile. Flowers in terminal or lateral raceme-like groups, each flower stalked. Calyx 5-partite and divided to the base, persistent when in fruit. Corolla violet at first, turning red-brown. Corolla tube longer than calyx and about 6 mm wide, with 5 short, triangular lobes, and with 5 scale-like projections from throat. Fruit of 4 nutlets, covered in hooked bristles.

Flowering season: May–June

Habitat: Dry, grassy sites, dunes, clearings, wasteland.

Distribution: Europe; Asia.

Active ingredients: Pyrrolizidine-alkaloids, allantoin, tannins, essential oil, mucilage.

Uses: To treat inflamed veins and sports injuries.

NB: Do not prepare or use at home because pyrrolizidine-alkaloids can affect the kidneys.

Bittersweet/Woody Nightshade* ☠

Solanum dulcamara

(Nightshade Family)

Scrambling perennial to 2 m tall, with woody base to stem. Leaves stalked, oval to lanceolate, often heart-shaped at the base or with 1 or 2 lobes, otherwise entire. Flowers in long-stalked panicle-like, mostly drooping clusters. Calyx 5-toothed and persistent, with roundly ovate teeth. Corolla 0.8–1.2 cm across, fused at the base and opening into 5 spreading or reflexed lobes. Stamens 5, with yellow anthers. Fruit a drooping berry, green at first, ripening to bright red.

Flowering season: June–Sep

Habitat: Hedges, wet woodland, banks, clearings, marsh, fen.

Distribution: Europe; much of Asia.

Active ingredients: Alkaloids, saponins, tannins.

Uses: In homeopathy to treat rheumatism, colds and skin rashes. Also used for asthma.

NB: Poisonous. Do not collect or use.

128 Vervain* ☒

Verbena officinalis

(Vervain Family)

Hairy perennial to 80 cm tall, with rectangular stem, branched above and roughly hairy along the ridges, otherwise hairless. Leaves opposite; lower leaves pinnately lobed or toothed, upper leaves toothed. Inflorescence a thin, loose spike of pale pink flowers with glandular hairs in the axils and on calyx. Corolla 3–5 mm long, tubular, with a 5-lobed, 2-lipped opening. Calyx 2 mm long, tubular, with 4–5 lobes.

Flowering season: July–Sep

Habitat: Footpaths, roadsides, wasteland, meadows.

Distribution: Most of Europe; much of Asia; N Africa. In BI commonest in S Britain.

Active ingredients: Verbenaline (glycoside), tannins, adenosine, some essential oil, silicic acid.

Uses: In homeopathy to treat epilepsy, insomnia, nervous complaints.

Further uses: A traditional aphrodisiac. Leaves yield hair tonic and eyewash. On poultice for skin ulcers and wounds.

129 Wall Germander* ✤

Teucrium chamaedrys

(Mint Family)

Evergreen dwarf shrub, to 30 cm tall, with a woody base to the hairy stem. Leaves opposite, oval, toothed, with musty smell when crushed, about as long as flowers. Inflorescence nodding to one side. Flowers mostly clustered in the axils of the upper leaves and with short stalks. Calyx bell shaped, 6–8 mm long, more or less regularly 5-lobed, weakly 2-lipped and hairy. Corolla 10–12 mm long with only the lower lip obvious (upper lip divided into 2 and the lobes deflected to the sides. See drawing on p. 58). Stamens and style projecting.

Flowering season: July–Aug

Habitat: Rocky sites, dry grassland, open woodland, walls.

Distribution: Much of Europe; Turkey; N Africa. Doubtfully native in Britain, naturalised from gardens.

Active ingredients: Essential oil, tannins, bitters, polyphenols.

Uses: Used formerly to treat digestive and gallbladder disorders, and loss of appetite; externally to bathe wounds. Also for gout and rheumatism.

Further uses: A constituent of some tonic wines and vermouths.

128

129

130 Betony* ⊛   *Stachys officinalis*

(Mint Family)

Perennial, to 70 cm tall, with square stems. Lower leaves stalked, narrowly oval, coarsely toothed, with heart-shaped base. Stem leaves in opposite pairs (usually 2 or 3 pairs). Inflorescence spike-like, made up of whorls of pinkish-purple flowers. Calyx 5–7 mm long, with 5 teeth, edged with bristles. Corolla 1–1.5 cm long, with flat upper lip and somewhat longer, 3-lobed lower lip. Anthers not exceeding upper lip.

Flowering season: July–Sep

Habitat: Dry grassland, meadows, open woods.

Distribution: Most of Europe; W Asia; N Africa. Common in England and Wales; rarer in Ireland and N Scotland.

Active ingredients: Tannins, bitters, betaine.

Uses: In homeopathy (occasionally) to treat asthma. Infusion is mildly sedative and a nerve tonic; also for migraine. Also used to treat diarrhoea and indigestion.

Home use tips: For diarrhoea and intestinal problems, and as gargle. Infuse 1 teaspoonful for 15 minutes in 250 ml boiling water. Drink 1–3 cups daily; or use as a gargle.

131
132 Motherwort* ☒   *Leonurus cardiaca*

(Mint Family)

Hairy, branched perennial growing to 1.5 m, with rectangular stem. Leaves stalked, in opposite pairs; lower leaves deeply lobed, upper leaves smaller, lobed or entire. Flowers grouped in whorls in leaf axils. Calyx 5–8 mm long, funnel-shaped, with 5 spine-tipped lobes, and weakly 2-lipped. Corolla pinkish-purple, 8–10 mm long, with hairy hood, short tube and 3-lobed lower lip.

Flowering season: June–Oct

Habitat: Footpaths, scrub, waste ground, dry pasture.

Distribution: Asia; Europe; N America (introduced). In BI introduced, formerly grown as medicinal herb; thinly scattered.

Active ingredients: Cardiac glycosides, bitters, tannins, alkaloids (including stachydrine), flavonoids, traces of essential oils.

Uses: In conventional and homeopathic medicine to regulate heartbeat and blood pressure. Also appears to reduce blood fat levels. Also used to contract uterus after birth, regulate periods and ease menopausal symptoms.

Home use tips: For nervous heart problems. Infuse 2 teaspoonsful commercial preparation in 250 ml boiling water for 10 minutes. Drink 1 cup daily.

NB: Rather rare. Do not collect. Also avoid in pregnancy as stachydrine can induce contractions.

130

131
132

133 Wild Marjoram* ✿   *Origanum vulgare*
(Mint Family)

Hairy, aromatic, branching perennial to 50 cm tall. Leaves opposite, oval; lower leaves stalked, upper leaves almost unstalked. Flowers pink, purple or (rarely) white, clustered into heads at the ends of stems and also in whorls lower down. Flower-bracts 3–6 mm long, red or purple. Calyx bell-shaped, 2.5–3.5 mm long, with 5 triangular even teeth. Corolla 2-lipped, 4–7 mm long, with 5 rounded lobes.

Flowering season: July–Oct

Habitat: Dry grassland, banks, dry open woodland, sunny wood margins and hedges.

Distribution: Most of Europe; Asia. In BI locally common.

Active ingredients: Essential oil, triterpene, bitters, tannins.

Uses: For bad coughs, whooping cough and intestinal problems.

Further uses: As herb. Finely chopped in salads. Makes a delicious jelly. Also makes a herbal tea, and formerly used to flavour ale.

Home use tips: For coughs, to stimulate appetite and to treat diarrhoea. Infuse 1 teaspoonful in 250 ml boiling water for 10 minutes. Take 1 cup, twice daily, sweetened with honey.

Note: This species is the herb oregano. The herb marjoram is Sweet Marjoram ✿ (*O. majorana*, 134), or Pot Marjoram ✿ (*O. onites*).

134 Sweet (Garden) Marjoram ✿ *Origanum majorana*
(Mint Family)

Aromatic and hairy, growing to 50 cm; stem much branched. Leaves 0.5–2 cm long, opposite, spoon-shaped or narrowly obovate, short-stalked, entire. White or pinkish flowers in panicles, extending down stems. Flowers mostly enclosed by bracts. Calyx 2.5 mm long, with a single lip. Corolla 4 mm long, with short, 2-lobed upper lip and longer 3-toothed lower lip.

Flowering season: July–Sep

Habitat: Dry, rocky sites; open pine woods; much planted.

Distribution: N Africa; Turkey; Cyprus; east to India. Widely cultivated and naturalised.

Active ingredients: Essential oil, bitters, tannins.

Uses: For loss of appetite, digestive problems; also for coughs, whooping cough and asthma. In homeopathy to treat female sexual disorders.

Further uses: Popular culinary herb; sweeter and spicier than oregano or Pot Marjoram. Tea aids digestion, soothes nerves and headaches and encourages menstruation.

Home use tips: To improve digestion, to treat flatulence; also externally for mouth infections and to treat wounds. Infuse 1–2 teaspoonsful in 250 ml boiling water for 5 minutes. Drink 1–2 cups daily; externally as gargle or wash.

Similar species: Pot Marjoram ✿ (*O. onites*) a native of Sicily, the Balkans and Crete. White flowers in broad clusters. Used as herb; rather milder than oregano.

135 # Summer Savory ✿   *Satureja hortensis*

(Mint Family)

Aromatic hairy annual, to 25 cm tall, with upright, branching stem. Leaves opposite, narrow and rounded, 1–3 cm long, without obvious stalk. Flowers very short-stalked, in axils of upper leaves, mainly nodding to one side. Calyx 3–4 mm long, bell-shaped, with 5 lanceolate, pointed teeth. Corolla 4–6 mm long, pink or white, with short tube, short upper lip and longer 3-lobed lower lip.

Flowering season: July–Sep

Habitat: Sunny sites on well-drained soil; much planted.

Distribution: Mediterranean region.

Active ingredients: Essential oil, tannins.

Uses: To treat flatulence, diarrhoea and digestive disorders, and generally to improve digestion. Flowering tops make an astringent gargle, and facial steam improves oily skin.

Further uses: Popular herb for bean dishes and other vegetables, and as garnish for stews. Counteracts the flatulence caused by beans. Also used to flavour salami and some digestive wines and liqueurs.

Home use tips: For digestive disorders. Infuse 2 teaspoonsful in 250 ml boiling water for 10 minutes. Drink 2–3 cups daily.

Similar species: Winter Savory° ✿ (*S. montana*) of S Europe, is introduced and rare in BI, naturalised on some old walls.

136 # Peppermint° ✿   *Mentha x piperita*

(Mint Family)   *(M. aquatica x M. spicata)*

Hairy or hairless perennial, to 90 cm tall, with erect, often red-tinged stems and characteristic peppermint smell. Leaves opposite, narrowly ovate to lanceolate, with sharp, but not deep teeth. Flowers stalked, in the axils of upper leaves, forming long, pyramidal or cylindrical heads. Calyx bell-shaped, 2 mm long, 5-toothed and weakly 2-lipped. Corolla pinkish-lilac, longer than calyx, 4-lobed.

Flowering season: July–Sep

Habitat: Damp ground, waste land. Widely planted.

Distribution: Europe; America (introduced). In BI scattered as native, also as garden escape.

Active ingredients: Essential oils, notably menthol, tannins, flavonoids.

Uses: Medicinally for stomach, intestinal, liver and gallbladder complaints.

Further uses: To flavour foods, sauces and desserts, sweets, toothpaste and medicines. Peppermint oil is mildly anaesthetic and antiseptic. Inhaled, the oil treats nausea.

Home use tips: For digestive disorders, flatulence and nausea. Infuse 1 teaspoonful in 250 ml boiling water for 10 minutes. 1 cup as required.

Similar species: The mints are a difficult group to identify, and several are variable. Eau de Cologne Mint ✿ is a hairless variety of Peppermint (var. *citrata*), with a fine perfume. Other garden mints, also of hybrid origin, are widely grown and naturalised. The commonest cultivated mint in BI is Spearmint° ✿ (*M. spicata*) which is almost hairless, with narrow leaves. Round-leaved Mint° ✿, *M. sauveolens*, with unstalked, rounded leaves, felty beneath, and an apply scent. In Britain, mainly SW England and Wales.

NB: Do not give Peppermint tea to young children (contains menthol).

137 Horse Mint/Long-leaved Mint ⊗

(Mint Family)   *Mentha longifolia*

A hairy mint with grey foliage, growing to 1 m tall. Stem rectangular and branching. Leaves opposite, sessile, narrowly ovate to lanceolate, 5–10 cm long, mostly sharply toothed. Flowers lilac or white, in dense, terminal spikes.

Flowering season: July–Sep

Habitat: Damp habitats.

Distribution: Much of Europe; W and C Asia; N Africa. Does not occur wild in BI.

Active ingredients: Essential oils, tannins.

Uses: Used medicinally like Peppermint (136), mainly in S Europe, Asia and N Africa.

Further uses: In N Africa to make a strong, bitter tea.

138 Water Mint*

(Mint Family)   *Mentha aquatica*

Aromatic perennial to 80 cm tall with characteristic minty smell. Stem almost hairless or softly hairy. Leaves short-stalked, oval, toothed, with 4–6 pairs of arched lateral veins. Flowers stalked, at the end of stem or in the axils of the uppermost leaves, in fairly dense clusters. Calyx tubular, 4 mm long, 5-lobed. Corolla 5–7 mm long with a ring of hairs in the tube and 4 even corolla lobes. With 4 stamens, protruding outside corolla.

Flowering season: July–Oct

Habitat: Banks, wet meadows, wet woodland, marshes, by ditches and ponds.

Distribution: Most of Europe; most of Asia; N and S Africa. In BI common throughout.

Active ingredients: Essential oils (only a little menthol), tannins.

Uses: Used previously like Peppermint (136).

139 Pennyroyal* ⚥⊗ ☠

(Mint Family)   *Mentha pulegium*

Aromatic perennial, often creeping, growing to 60 cm tall. Stem branched, almost hairless or sparsely hairy. Leaves short-stalked, oval, with only 1–3 pairs of obvious lateral veins. Flowers lilac, short-stalked, in dense but widely separated clusters in the axils of upper leaves. Calyx tubular and hairy, 3 mm long, 2-lipped. Corolla 5–7 mm long, with 4 more or less equal lobes. Stamens 4, protruding.

Flowering season: July–Oct

Habitat: Damp grassland, pond sides.

Distribution: Much of Europe; W Asia; N Africa. In BI very local, mainly in S England, S Wales and Ireland; often near the sea.

Active ingredients: Essential oils, notably pulegon and menthol, tannins.

Uses: Formerly to treat menstrual problems.

Further uses: Repels insects.

NB: No longer used because pulegon is poisonous. Can cause miscarriage.

140 **(Common) Thyme** * ✿   *Thymus vulgaris*
(Mint Family)

Much-branched low evergreen shrub, growing to 30 cm, with rectangular hairy stem. Leaves opposite, 5–9 mm long, linear or elliptic, with rolled margins and felty hairs beneath. Flowers in clusters of 3–6, in axils of upper leaves, forming a spike-like inflorescence. Calyx tubular, stiffly hairy and 3–5 mm long; upper lip short, with triangular central lobe and lanceolate side lobes; lower lip longer, 2-lobed. Corolla lilac or pink, 4–6 mm long, with 3-lobed lower lip.

Flowering season: May–Oct
Habitat: Rocky slopes, dry grassland, maquis.
Distribution: W Mediterranean. Introduced and naturalised further north, including BI, where scattered, mainly in S England.
Active ingredients: Essential oils, notably thymol, tannins, bitters, flavones.
Uses: As expectorant and mild anaesthetic for coughs, whooping cough, and acute and chronic bronchitis. In homeopathy for coughs and intestinal complaints.
Further uses: As culinary herb. Thyme oil also used in mouthwashes.
Home use tips: For coughs and digestive disorders. Boil 1 teaspoonful in 250 ml water. Drink 3 cups daily, sweetened with honey for coughs.

141 **Large Thyme** *   *Thymus pulegioides*
(Mint Family)

Aromatic, creeping plant with stems up to 40 cm long, either growing along the ground or arching upwards. Flowering stems noticeably 4-angled, mostly hairy only on the ridges. Leaves opposite, oval to spoon-shaped, narrowing towards stalk and with long bristles at base. Flowers in groups in the axils of the upper leaves, either in whorls or in denser heads. Calyx 2-lipped. Corolla 2-lipped, 3–6 mm long.

Flowering season: June–Oct
Habitat: Dry grassland, footpaths, scrub, walls.
Distribution: C and N Europe (except far N and NW). In Britain common only in southern areas.
Active ingredients: Essential oils, bitters, tannins, flavones.
Uses: To treat coughs.
Further uses: As culinary herb.
Home use tips: For coughs and digestive disorders. Infuse 1–2 teaspoonful in 250 ml water for 10 minutes. Drink 3 cups daily.
Similar species: Sand (Breckland) Thyme° (*T. serpyllum*) has long, creeping rounded stems, hairy on all sides and narrowly lanceolate leaves. Only in sandy parts of C Europe. Also a rare British species, found in the East Anglian Breckland. Wild Thyme°(*T. polytrichus* [*T. praecox*]) has long, creeping stems, rounded flowering stems and an even distribution of hairs. Leaves rounded to oval. Common in Britain. In C Europe mainly in the mountains.

140

141

Foxglove* ☠ ✿⊛

Digitalis purpurea

(Figwort Family)

Biennial or perennial, to 1.5 m tall, with unbranched, upright stem, covered with grey felty hairs. Leaves oval to lanceolate, toothed; lower leaves stalked, forming a rosette, upper leaves unstalked. Inflorescence a raceme, with flowers nodding to one side. Calyx 5-lobed. Sepals oval, with glandular hairs. Latter also present on flower stalks and upper stem. Corolla drooping downwards, with inflated tube and short, 2-lobed margin, pink, purple or (more rarely) white, dark spots inside. Lower lip 5 cm long, 3-lobed (upper lip shorter).

Flowering season: June–Aug

Habitat: Open woods, clearings, hillsides, footpaths, waste land; on acid soils (but also grows in calcareous soil in gardens).

Distribution: Much of Europe; common garden plant and garden escape.

Active ingredients: Cardiac glycosides, saponins.

Uses: In conventional medicine as standard preparation for cardiac problems. In homeopathy to treat weak heartbeat, kidney trouble, depression, insomnia and migraine.

NB: Poisonous. Do not collect or use.

Common Valerian*

Valeriana officinalis

(Valerian Family)

Variable, erect perennial growing to 1.8 m tall, with opposite leaves. Basal leaves large and pinnate; stem leaves somewhat smaller. Flowers pink, in umbel-like many-flowered clusters. Corolla 3–6 mm long, tubular at the base, becoming funnel-shaped and 3–4 lobed. Calyx with thickened margin.

Flowering season: May–Sep

Habitat: Open woods, tall herb communities, wet meadows, ditches, river banks.

Distribution: Most of Europe.

Active ingredients: Valepotriates, valeric acids, alkaloids, essential oils.

Uses: In conventional and homeopathic medicine to treat nervous tension, insomnia and nervous stomach and intestine problems. Also for headaches, irritable bowel syndrome and eczema.

Further uses: The root is used in some perfumes.

Home use tips: For insomnia. Infuse 2 teaspoonsful in 250 ml cold water for 10–12 hours. Drink 1 cup 2 or 3 times daily.

Note: Tests have shown anti-tumour activity.

Red Valerian* ⊛

Centranthus ruber

(Valerian Family)

Erect hairless perennial to 1 m tall. Leaves grey-green, oval or lanceolate; lower leaves stalked, upper leaves opposite and unstalked. Flowers red, pink or white, short-stalked, in dense compound cymes. Corolla with 10 mm long tube and obvious spur. Stamen 1, stigma 1. Fruit with feathery pappus (from calyx) when ripe.

Flowering season: May–July

Habitat: Dry, sunny sites, cliffs, walls, rocks, embankments.

Distribution: S and W Europe. In BI introduced and naturalised.

Active ingredients: Valepotriates.

Uses: In homeopathy to treat nervous problems.

146 Hemp-agrimony*   *Eupatorium cannabinum*

(Daisy Family)

Hairy perennial, to 1.5 m tall, with firm, erect, leafy stems. Leaves opposite, with 3–5 lanceolate, rather unevenly toothed segments. Flowerheads numerous, pinkish-purple or pink, in compound, umbel-like panicles. Involucral bracts small and leaf-like. All florets tubular with 5 teeth. Fruit about 3 mm long, with pappus of hairs.

Flowering season: July–Sep

Habitat: Wet woodland, riverbanks, pond margins, tall herb communities, waste land.

Distribution: Most of Europe; W Asia; N Africa. In BI throughout, but local and mostly coastal in Scotland.

Active ingredients: Eupatoriopicrine, euparine, lactucerol, tannins, saponins, essential oil.

Uses: To treat flu-like infections and to support antibiotic treatment. To aid recovery during convalescence. Diuretic and immune system stimulant.

Note: Tests have revealed anti-tumour activity in this genus.

147 Cone-flower ❀   *Echinacea angustifolia*

(Daisy Family)

Hairy rhizomatous perennial to 60 cm tall, with erect, unbranched stems. Leaves lanceolate and entire, with 3 veins; lower leaves with short stalks, upper leaves unstalked. Flowerheads usually solitary, about 5–7 cm across, on long stems. Involucre cup-shaped; bracts with bristly hairs, arranged in 2 rows. Central tubular florets in cone-shaped cluster, overtopped by bristly scales. Ray florets pale purple, linear, 2–3.5 cm long; drooping. Fruit rectangular, with crowning pappus.

Flowering season: May–Aug

Habitat: Dry, open woodland, prairie.

Distribution: Central N America. Planted in Europe.

Active ingredients: Echinacine, echinacoside, essential oil, resin, bitters.

Uses: Externally as ointment to treat wounds and skin complaints. In homeopathy to support recovery from flu and colds; also for skin problems. Root extract is antibiotic, anti-viral and reduces inflammation. This flower is under investigation in the search for a cure for AIDS, because it is one of the most effective herbal stimulants of the immune system.

Similar species: Purple Cone-flower ❀ (*E. purpurea*) has toothed leaves and narrower flower scales; petals less drooping.

Greater Burdock*

Arctium lappa

(Daisy Family)

Robust, hairy biennial, to 1.5 m tall, with furrowed, branching stem. Leaves stalked, broadly oval and pointed, to 50 cm long, green above, with felty hairs beneath. Flowerheads purple (rarely white), dense and rounded, 3–3.5 cm across. Involucral bracts with hooked spines. Florets all tubular. The fruiting heads (burrs) with their hooked bracts are dispersed by animals.

Flowering season: July–Sep

Habitat: Footpaths, waste ground, river banks, scrub, wood clearings.

Distribution: Most of Europe except far N; N and W Asia. Common in BI.

Active ingredients: Essential oil, fatty oil, tannins, polyacetylene, mucilage, inulin.

Uses: Young shoots and roots infused to make a tonic. Root said to prevent colds and flu; also used to treat rheumatism and cystitis. Should not be taken when pregnant. Externally the oil can be used to treat dandruff and hair loss. In homeopathy for skin complaints, including eczema.

Home use tips: As blood-purifier, and externally as skin tonic. Infuse 2 teaspoonsful in 250 ml cold water for 5 hours. Then boil for 1 minute. Drink 3 cups daily; externally as a wash.

Similar species: Lesser Burdock° (*A. minus*) has rather smaller flowerheads. Similar habitat and distribution.

Woolly Burdock

Arctium tomentosum

(Daisy Family)

Hairy biennial, to 1 m tall, with branching stem. Leaves broad, heart-shaped or rounded, to 50 cm long, green above, with felty hairs beneath, and with pith-filled stalk. Inflorescences (top right) in umbel-like cluster, each rounded and about 2–3 cm across. Bracts covered in cobweb-like hairs. Florets all tubular, purple.

Flowering season: July–Sep

Habitat: Footpaths, waste ground, scrub.

Distribution: Europe, except far N; N Asia. In BI a rare casual only.

Active ingredients and uses: See Greater Burdock (148).

151 Cotton Thistle* ⊗

Onopordum acanthium

(Daisy Family)

Biennial thistle, growing to 2.5 m, covered with cottony hairs. Stem erect, with spiny wings, branching towards top. Leaves shallowly lobed, spiny; lower leaves short-stalked, upper leaves joining stem with winged margin. Flowerheads purple (occasionally white), solitary and terminal, 3–6 cm across, surrounded by spreading, spiny bracts.

Flowering season: July–Sep

Habitat: Roadsides, waste ground, embankments, fields.

Distribution: Most of Europe; Asia. N. America (introduced). In BI probably introduced; scattered, mainly in SE England.

Active ingredients: Bitters, tannins, flavone-glycosides.

Uses: In homeopathy for heart and circulatory problems. Root decoction reduces mucus discharge.

Further uses: Young stems and flowerheads can be eaten.

Note: This thistle, sometimes rather misleadingly (given its distribution) called Scots Thistle, forms the emblem of Scotland.

152 Milk Thistle*

Silybum marianum

(Daisy Family)

Biennial thistle, to 1.5 m, with unwinged stems; hairless or downy. Leaves shiny green, with white marbling, unstalked, lobed and spiny. Upper leaves with spiny bases encircling stem. Flowerheads purple, solitary, 4–5 cm across, surrounded by a halo of long, spiny bracts. Fruits 6–7 mm long, smooth, with whitish pappus.

Flowering season: June–Sep

Habitat: Footpaths, waste ground, fields, rocky slopes.

Distribution: S Europe; Caucasus; W Asia; N Africa. In BI introduced; frequent casual.

Active ingredients: Bitters, flavonoids, essential oil, silymarin.

Uses: Liver complaints, including jaundice, infections, cirrhosis. Also to treat coughs, travel sickness and depression.

Note: Silymarin, from the seeds, has been shown to protect the liver from toxins, including alcohol.

153 Globe Artichoke ⊗

Cynara scolymus

(Daisy Family)

Thistle-like perennial to 1.8 m tall, with thick, branching stem. Leaves large; lower leaves stalked and entire, upper leaves unstalked and lobed. Flowerheads very large, with thick base and leathery, oval bracts, each fleshy towards the base. Florets tubular, violet.

Flowering season: July

Habitat: Only known in cultivation, unknown in the wild.

Distribution: Originated around Mediterranean. In BI only as occasional casual.

Active ingredients: Bitters, tannins, flavonoids.

Uses: Medicinally to increase bile secretion and to lower cholesterol levels in the blood. Also for anaemia, liver damage and hepatitis.

Further uses: Fleshy bracts and receptacle eaten as vegetable. Known as a food plant by the Greeks and Romans.

Lily-of-the-valley* ☘⊛☒   *Convallaria majalis*

(Lily Family)

Hairless perennial to 30 cm tall. Lower leaves scale-like. 2 upper leaves broadly lanceolate, sheathing the stem at base, and 10–20 cm long, with parallel veins. Inflorescence a one-sided, long-stalked raceme growing up from between the leaves. Bracts very small and shorter than flower stalk. Flowers white and fragrant, nodding and bell-shaped, 5–7 mm long, with 6 fused perianth segments with small outwardly-directed lobes. 6 stamens with yellow anthers. Ovary superior, with short style. Fruit a 2–6 seeded round red berry.

Flowering season: May–June

Habitat: Deciduous woods, scrub, hedgerows.

Distribution: Most of Europe (in the S only in the mountains) eastwards to C Asia. In Britain native in calcareous woodland, but grown in gardens and often naturalised.

Active ingredients: Various cardiac glycosides, saponins.

Uses: In conventional and homeopathic medicine for heart problems, in particular those involving heart muscle and heart-related fluid retention.

Further uses: Flower water is astringent skin wash.

NB: Plant is poisonous and protected. Do not collect or use.

White False Helleborine ☘   *Veratrum album*

(Lily Family)

Erect, rather robust perennial to 1.5 m tall with unbranched stem, densely hairy, especially towards the top. Leaves alternate, elliptic, with parallel veins, sessile and encircling the stem with sheath at base; hairless above, softly hairy below. Flowers whitish or yellow-green, in long spike-like inflorescences, branched towards the base. Flowers short-stalked, 0.8–1.5 cm across, with 6 segments. Stamens 6. Ovary superior, with 3 short styles. Fruit an elongated capsule, 10–15 mm long, splitting to release winged seeds.

Flowering season: June–Aug

Habitat: Damp meadows, pasture, fens; mainly on high ground.

Distribution: Finland, Norway and mountains of C Europe.

Active ingredients: Alkaloids, notably protoveratrine and germerine.

Uses: In homeopathy for diarrhoea and food poisoning, weak circulation, sciatica and neuralgia. Also used to treat hypertension.

Further uses: As insecticide and in veterinary medicine.

158 Ramsons/Wild Garlic*

Allium ursinum

(Lily Family)

Hairless perennial to about 50 cm tall, with erect, unbranched stem; usually grows in large colonies. Leaves all basal, normally 2, to 20 cm long, broadly lanceolate, pointed and long-stalked. Inflorescence a terminal umbel, at first encased in papery bracts which soon fall away. Flowers stalked and star-shaped, with 6 perianth segments 8–12 cm long. 6 stamens. Fruit a 3–lobed capsule.

Flowering season: Apr–June

Habitat: Damp woods, hedges, shady damp meadows, streamsides.

Distribution: Much of Europe, east to the Caucasus; N Asia.

Active ingredients: Essential oils (containing sulphur), vitamin C, allicin, iron.

Uses: To treat digestive problems, rheumatism, high blood pressure and asthma.

Further uses: Fresh leaves in salads, soups and with soft cheese.

Home use tips: For loss of appetite or digestive disorders. Eat fresh leaves, chopped up small.

NB: Easily confused when not flowering with the poisonous Lily-of-the-valley, but the garlic smell of Ramsons when crushed is distinctive.

Note: Many species of the genus *Allium* contain strong-smelling and sharp-tasting oils in all parts of the plant. The value of these compounds to the plants is not known for certain but they probably help protect them from being eaten by animals. Ramsons, along with Garlic, is one of the most strong smelling of all *Allium* species.

159 Garlic* ⊛

Allium sativum

(Lily Family)

Hairless perennial to 70 cm tall. Bulb made up of a number of 'cloves' (the part normally eaten) enclosed in a single papery skin. Stem erect and unbranched, with leaves in lower half. Leaves linear, pointed, keeled below, to 12 mm across, and encircling the stem with sheath at base. Inflorescence umbel-like, few-flowered, often with small aerial bulbils instead of flowers. Individual flowers long-stalked, with 6 pinkish-white or greenish-white 3 mm long perianth segments. Stamens 6, shorter than petals.

Flowering season: June–Aug

Habitat: In Europe and elsewhere mainly cultivated (in Egypt for the past 5,000 years), or an escape onto waste ground.

Distribution: Originally from C Asia. In BI introduced and occasionally seen as casual or garden escape.

Active ingredients: Essential oils (containing sulphur), vitamin C, iron.

Uses: In conventional and homeopathic medicine for intestinal problems, bronchial complaints, high blood pressure and arteriosclerosis. Also used as an antiseptic, antispasmodic and to kill parasitic worms.

Further uses: Well known as culinary herb. Repels insects. Endowed with magical properties in many cultures.

Home use tips: For intestinal problems, bronchial complaints, and to prevent arteriosclerosis. Take 2 cloves daily. Can be taken in tablet form to avoid tainting the breath.

158

159

160 Onion* ⊗   *Allium cepa*
(Lily Family)

Hairless biennial (often grown as annual) to 1.2 m tall. Bulb has reddish or
brownish skin, with or without side-bulbs. Stem erect, hollow, inflated
towards base. Leaves only at base, inflated, shorter than stem. Large, round
inflorescence, made up of many greenish-white flowers. Stamens 6.

Flowering season: June–Aug

Habitat: In Europe and elsewhere mainly cultivated (a staple food since the
time of the Ancient Egyptians), or escape onto waste ground.

Distribution: Originally from C Asia. In BI introduced and common in
gardens; often seen as casual.

Active ingredients: Essential oils (containing sulphur), thiopropionaldehyde
(causes eyes to water), vitamin C, iron.

Uses: In homeopathy to treat colds, bronchitis and intestinal problems.

Further uses: Long cultivated and eaten as vegetable or flavouring plant.

Note: This species includes Shallot. Other *Allium* species are Chives° ⊗ *(A.
schoenoprasum)*, Welsh Onion ⊗ *(A. fistulosum)* and Leek ⊗ *(A. porrum)*.

161 Sea Squill ☠   *Urginea maritima*
(Lily Family)

Hairless perennial to 1.5 m tall. Bulb to 15 cm across and 2.5 kg, covered
in thin, brown skin and with top emerging from ground. Stem erect and
simple. Leaves lanceolate and basal, produced after flowering.
Inflorescence a dense terminal spike-like, many-flowered raceme, to 40
cm long. Flowers stalked, 6-partite, each segment to 8 mm long, white,
with greenish-purple central vein. Fruit a rounded capsule.

Flowering season: Aug–Oct

Habitat: Dry, rocky slopes, dunes.

Distribution: Mediterranean coasts.

Active ingredients: Cardiac glycosides.

Uses: In conventional medicine for certain cardiac conditions and
heart-related fluid retention. In homeopathy for weak heartbeat and
bronchitis. Also has diuretic properties.

NB: Poisonous. Do not use.

162 Buckwheat* ⊗   *Fagopyrum esculentum*
(Dock Family)

Very sparsely hairy annual to 1 m tall. Stems little-branched and often tinged
pink or red. Leaves alternate, heart- or arrow-shaped, with sheathing stipule at
base; lower leaves long-stalked, upper leaves short-stalked. Flowers in
long-stalked clusters in the leaf axils. Perianth segments 5, white (more rarely
pale pink), 3–4 mm long. Fruit a 3-angled nutlet, brown when ripe.

Flowering season: July–Oct

Habitat: Waste ground; cultivated.

Distribution: Asia. In BI casual, formerly much grown.

Active ingredients: Rutin (a flavonol-glycoside), fagopyrine.

Uses: To treat varicose veins, haemorrhoids, arteriosclerosis and retinal
bleeding. In homeopathy for skin problems and infections.

Further uses: The nuts are cooked and eaten, or ground to make flour.

163 Ornamental Rhubarb ⊛   *Rheum palmatum*

(Dock Family)

Large perennial to 1.5 m tall with robust stem, branching towards top.
Rootstock thick, reddish and woody. Leaves very large, with long, thick,
fleshy, rounded stalks. Blade rounded, heart-shaped and palmately lobed
and veined. Lobes acute and toothed. Flowers small, in large panicles, in
the axils of upper leaves. Perianth 6-partite, white or pale pink. Stamens 9.
Fruit a small 3-sided nutlet.

Flowering season: May–June
Habitat: Grassy places; gardens.
Distribution: NE Asia. In BI grown in gardens; occasional escape.
Active ingredients: Anthraquinone, tannins.
Uses: In conventional medicine for stomach and intestinal problems. In
homeopathy to treat diarrhoea. The related Medicinal Rhubarb has been
used in Chinese medicine for 3,000 years, among other things for liver
complaints, fever, and as an anti-inflammatory and antiseptic compress.
Further uses: As ingredient of alcoholic digestive bitters.
Similar species: Medicinal Rhubarb (*R. officinale*) grows to 3 m and has
rounded leaves, with 5 short lobes. Rhubarb° ⊛, the commonly planted
crop, is *R. rhabarbarum*, with oval, entire leaves and edible leaf-stalks. It is
native of E Asia.

164 Common Chickweed*   *Stellaria media*

(Pink Family)

One of the commonest weeds. Very variable in petal-size, habit and other
characters. Low-lying to erect, round-stemmed annual, growing to 40 cm
tall. Stems with 1 or 2 rows of hairs, the line of hairs on each successive
internode set at 90° further round stem. Leaves stalked, oval, pointed and
hairless, stalks sometimes whiskered. Upper leaves almost unstalked.
Flowers 5-partite, in the axils of green bracts. Sepals 2–5 mm long. Petals
shorter than sepals, or more or less equally long, divided almost to their
base. Stamens usually 3, but up to 10. Styles 3. Fruit a capsule, opening
with 6 teeth, measuring more than a third of capsule length.

Flowering season: Jan–Dec
Habitat: Fields, gardens, waste ground, footpaths.
Distribution: Worldwide.
Active ingredients: Saponin, vitamins A, B and C, calcium, potassium.
Uses: In homeopathy for rheumatism, arthritis and bronchitis.
Further uses: Eaten in salad, or as a soup or soup garnish. Tonic for cage
birds and poultry.
Home use tips: Internally for coughs, externally as a wash for wounds,
rashes or sores. Infuse 2 teaspoonsful in 250 ml boiling hot water for
5–10 minutes. Take 2 cups daily (warm).

163

164

165 Edible Love-in-a-mist ✿   *Nigella sativa*

(Buttercup Family)

Hairy annual to 45 cm tall, with simple or upright-branching stem. Leaves very short-stalked and feathery, with narrow leaflets. Flowers solitary and terminal. Sepals 5, petaloid, white, rounded, often greenish or bluish at tip. Petals nectary-like, usually 8, much shorter than sepals, 2-lobed, containing nectar at base. 5–9 carpels, fused for most of length. Fruit a 5–9-lobed capsule with black seeds.

Flowering season: July–Sep

Habitat: Waste ground; planted.

Distribution: W Asia to India. E Mediterranean.

Active ingredients: Saponin, bitters, essential and fatty oils.

Uses: Reduces flatulence, to treat diarrhoea, and against intestinal worms.

Further uses: Seeds (nutmeg-taste) used to flavour curries, vegetables and on baked products. Also used as insect repellent.

Home use tips: For flatulence and diarrhoea. Infuse 1 teaspoonful crushed seeds in 250 ml boiling hot water for 15 minutes. Drink 2 cups daily.

166 Traveller's Joy/Old Man's Beard*   *Clematis vitalba*

(Buttercup Family)

Alternative name comes from the white, feathery fruits. Liane-like climber with ridged stems to 30 m. Leaves opposite, stalked and with 3–5 weakly toothed leaflets. Clambers and twines up trees and in hedges, using leaves and leaf-stalks. Flowers stalked, in panicles, terminal on shoots or in leaf axils. Perianth segments 4, creamy white and hairy beneath. Stamens numerous. Fruit a cluster of feathery achenes.

Flowering season: June–Sep

Habitat: Woodland, scrub, hedgerows. Mainly on calcareous soils.

Distribution: W Asia; C and S Europe, north to Holland and BI.

Active ingredients: Protanemonine, anemonine.

Uses: In homeopathy to treat skin rashes, swollen glands, rheumatism, and male sexual disorders.

165

166

167 Garlic Mustard/Jack-by-the-hedge*

(Cabbage Family) *Alliaria petiolata*

Hairless biennial growing to 1 m tall, with erect stems, softly hairy towards base, smelling of garlic when crushed. Lower leaves stalked, heart-shaped and bluntly toothed; stem-leaves short-stalked and more triangular.
Flowers white, short-stalked, in racemes. Sepals 4, 2.5–3 mm long. Petals 4, 5–6 mm long. Stamens 6, 2 shorter and 4 longer ones. Fruit a narrow, pod-shaped capsule (siliqua), 3.5–6 cm long. Seeds dark brown, 3 mm long.
Flowering season: Apr–June
Habitat: Woodland edges, scrub, hedgerows; gardens.
Distribution: Europe; W Asia; N Africa.
Active ingredients: Mustard-oil glycosides, sulphur-rich essential oils, cardiac glycosides.
Uses: Antiseptic and anti-asthmatic. Earlier to treat bronchial complaints and worms. Not much used today. Also as poultice for ulcers and cuts.
Further uses: Leaves are a good addition to salads.

168 169 Common Scurvygrass*

(Cabbage Family) *Cochlearia officinalis*

Variable hairless biennial or perennial growing to about 50 cm tall, with erect, furrowed stems. Upper leaves unstalked and clasping stem; basal leaves stalked, heart-shaped and in a rosette. Flowers (below right) 4-partite, stalked, in elongating raceme. Sepals 1.5–2 mm long. Petals 4–5 mm long, narrow and obovate. Stamens 6, 2 shorter and 4 longer ones. Anthers yellow. Fruit (below left) stalked, rounded or oval, 3–7 mm.
Flowering season: May–June
Habitat: Saltmarshes, coastal rocks, salty sites inland.
Distribution: NW Europe; mainly coastal.
Active ingredients: Mustard-oil glycosides, bitters, tannins, vitamin C, minerals.
Uses: In homeopathy for eye infections and stomach cramp.
Similar species: English Scurvygrass° (*C. anglica*) has white flowers, and fruits to 14 mm. Common on coasts of BI and W Europe. Danish Scurvygrass° (*C. danica*) is a low-growing annual, with ivy-shaped lower leaves, stalked stem leaves and small, white or pale mauve flowers. Coastal, N and W Europe.
Note: The name comes from its traditional use as a source of vitamin C to combat the deficiency disease scurvy.

167

170 Horseradish* ✿   *Armoracia rusticana*

(Cabbage Family)

Robust, hairless perennial, to 1.5 m tall, with thick, fleshy root. Stem erect,
hollow, furrowed and branching. Lower leaves to 1 m long, long-stalked,
elliptic and toothed, with heart-shaped base. Stem leaves short-stalked, and
smaller. Flowers white, long-stalked and 4-partite; in large panicles in
upper part of stem. Sepals 2.5–3 mm long. Petals 5–7 mm long, obovate.
Fruit a pod-shaped capsule (silicula), 4–6 mm long.

Flowering season: May–July

Habitat: Waste ground, fields, streamsides; planted.

Distribution: W Asia. Introduced.

Active ingredients: Mustard-oil glycosides, volatile antibiotic substances,
vitamin C.

Uses: Antibiotic and expectorant. In conventional medicine as preparation
against respiratory and urinary infection. Oil from the root clears sinuses.
As poultice for rheumatism and bronchitis.

Further uses: Grated root as a sauce with meat, sausage and fish.

NB: **Do not externally as may cause a skin rash.**

171
172 Shepherd's-purse*   *Capsella bursa-pastoris*

(Cabbage Family)

Very variable, sparsely hairy annual plant growing to 40 cm, with upright,
often branching stems. Basal leaves in a rosette, stalked, mostly pinnately
lobed. Stem leaves encircling stem at base, with 2 pointed lobes. Upper
stem leaves simple. Flowers white, long-stalked, in loose, leafless racemes.
Stamens 1–2 mm long. Petals 4, 2–3 mm long. Fruit to 2 cm, stalked,
heart-shaped, with straight edges.

Flowering season: Mar–Dec

Habitat: Crops, paths, gardens, waste ground.

Distribution: Virtually worldwide.

Active ingredients: Flavone-glycosides, saponins, amines.

Uses: As antiseptic diuretic. Also for varicose veins, and to treat excess
bleeding. In homeopathy for gall-bladder and kidney problems.

Further uses: Leaves can be eaten in salads.

173 Watercress* ✺   *Rorippa nasturtium-aquaticum*

(Cabbage Family)

Virtually hairless perennial growing to 50 cm tall, with creeping stems, rooting at nodes, occasionally floating in water. Leaves pinnate, with 3–9 leaflets. Flowers white, in a short leafless raceme. Sepals 2–3 mm long, hairless. Petals 4, 3.5–5 mm long. Stamens 6, 2 short and 4 longer. Fruit a siliqua, 13–18 mm long and 1.8–2.5 mm broad, with the seeds arranged in 2 rows.

Flowering season: June–Sep

Habitat: Clear streams, ditches, ponds, wet flushes; also cultivated.

Distribution: Worldwide.

Active ingredients: Gluconasturtine (a mustard-oil glycoside), bitters, iodine, vitamin C.

Uses: Diuretic, expectorant. To aid digestion in cases of gall-bladder disorders. Traditionally to treat tuberculosis.

Further uses: In salads and soups.

Similar species: Narrow-fruited Watercress° (*R. microphylla*). This has a capsule 16–24 mm long and 1.2–1.8 mm thick, with seeds in a single row.

174 Round-leaved Sundew* ☒   *Drosera rotundifolia*

(Sundew Family)

Hairy insectivorous perennial to about 30 cm tall (usually smaller), with unstalked stems, and a rosette of long-stalked, spoon-shaped leaves. Leaf blade 5–10 mm broad, with sticky glandular hairs (1–5 mm long) above and along edges. Stem leafless, with a few-flowered inflorescence. Sepals 5, short and fused at base. Petals 4–6 mm long, white. Fruit a smooth capsule.

Flowering season: June–Aug

Habitat: Bogs, moors, wet heaths.

Distribution: Europe, Siberia, N America. In BI commonest in N and W.

Active ingredients: Droserone, flavonoids, naphtoquinone derivatives.

Uses: To treat coughs, whooping cough and bronchial asthma.

Similar species: Great Sundew° ☒ (*D. anglica*) has longer, erect, narrower leaves (blade 5–10 times as long as broad) and smooth capsule. In BI commonest in NW Ireland and NW Scotland. Oblong-leaved Sundew° ☒ (*D. intermedia*) has erect, spoon-shaped leaves (blades 2–3 times as long as broad) and capsule with longitudinal furrows. In BI mainly in W Scotland and W Ireland.

NB: Protected. Do not collect.

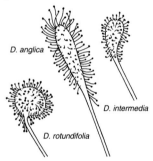

D. anglica

D. intermedia

D. rotundifolia

Leaves

173

174

175 Meadowsweet*

Filipendula ulmaria

(Rose Family)

Perennial to 2 m tall, with leafy stem, branched towards the top. Leaves pinnate, with 5–11 fine-toothed leaflets. Stem leaves dark green above, hairless, mostly with white felty hairs underneath. Flowers densely clustered in a much-branched, rather fluffy looking inflorescence. Sepals 1 mm long. Petals 5 or 6, rounded to oval, 2–5 mm long and yellowish-white in colour. Achenes smooth and twisted together in a spiral. Flowering season June–Aug

Habitat: Tall-herb communities, hay meadows, river banks, fens, ditches.

Distribution: Most of Europe, east to E Asia.

Active ingredients: Compounds of salicylic acid, flavone-glycosides, essential oil, tannins.

Uses: As diuretic and to treat fever, flu and rheumatism. Flower tea treats stomach ulcers and headaches.

Further uses: Used formerly to strew inside houses because of its pleasant smell. The leaves were added to wines and preserves. Regarded as sacred by the Druids.

Home use tips: Infuse 1–2 teaspoonful in 250 ml boiling hot water for 10 minutes. Drink 2 cups daily.

Similar species: Dropwort° (*F. vulgaris*). Leaves green on both sides, divided, with 21–81 roughly-toothed leaflets. 6 petals, 5–10 mm long. Achenes hairy, straight and erect. Dry grassland. Local on chalk and limestone in BI.

176 Wild Strawberry*

Fragaria vesca

(Rose Family)

Creeping, hairy perennial to 20 cm tall, with long, rooting runners. Leaves basal and long-stalked, 3-lobed, with roughly-toothed leaflets; the terminal tooth of the leaflet is longer than those on either side. Inflorescence with up to 5 flowers. Flowerstalks with appressed or erect hairs. Flowers white, 1–1.5 cm across, with 5 white petals, touching or slightly overlapping. The ripe fruit is a red, fleshy head with embedded achenes.

Flowering season: May–June

Habitat: Open woods, woodland edges, scrub.

Distribution: Most of Europe; N Asia.

Active ingredients: Tannins, essential oil, flavonols.

Uses: To treat diarrhoea. In homeopathy to treat chilblains.

Further uses: Ripe fruits have a delicate flavour.

Home use tips: For digestive problems and diarrhoea. Infuse 2 teaspoonful in 250 ml boiling hot water for 10 minutes. Drink 3 cups daily.

Similar species: Hautbois Strawberry (*F. muricata*) has an 8–15 flowered inflorescence, leafstalk with erect hairs, and flowers 1.5–2.5 cm across. Mainly C Europe. In BI introduced, but rare. Barren Strawberry° (*Potentilla sterilis*) has the end tooth of the leaflet noticeably smaller and shorter than the 2 neighbouring teeth. Flowers white, 1–1.5 cm across with 5 separated petals. Fruit not becoming fleshy when ripe.

175

176

177 Bramble/Blackberry* ⊛

Rubus fruticosus

(Rose Family)

Sturdy, spiny shrub to 2 m tall, often with arching, rounded or ridged branches, often rooting at tips, making natural impenetrable livestock-proof thickets or managed hedges. Leaves with prickly stalk, 3–5 lobed, with toothed leaflets; hairless, or hairy on undersides. Flowers in clusters at the ends of short side branches. Sepals 5, usually with downy hairs, turning back when in fruit. Petals white or pink. Stamens numerous. Fruit red at first, ripening black; a cluster of juicy drupes; breaking off with part of stalk.

Flowering season: May–Oct

Habitat: Woodland, hedgerows, scrub, heath.

Distribution: Most of Europe; Asia; N Africa.

Active ingredients: Tannins, flavone, organic acids, vitamin C.

Uses: For diarrhoea. Also skin rashes, eczema and mouth or throat infections.

Further uses: Tasty fruits eaten and also used to make drinks, including wine.

Home use tips: An infusion for use as gargle for mouth or throat infections. Infuse 2 teaspoonful in 250 ml boiling hot water for 15 minutes.

Note: The taxonomy of this group is very complex, with many forms and hybrids, often of garden origin.

178 Raspberry* ⊛

Rubus idaeus

(Rose Family)

Perennial shrub to 1.5 m tall, with biennial bristly stems, with whitish bloom when young. Leaves pinnate, with 5–7 leaflets which are toothed and with white downy hairs. Flowers in loose clusters. Sepals turning back after flowering. Petals white and narrow. Fruit red, dropping away from receptacle when ripe.

Flowering season: May–July

Habitat: Woods, scrub, heath, waste ground.

Distribution: Throughout northern hemisphere.

Active ingredients: Tannins, flavone, organic acids, vitamin C, fragarine.

Uses: Used traditionally to ease childbirth. Tea reduces menstrual pains.

Further uses: Tasty fruits eaten and also used to make drinks, including wine.

179 180 Blackthorn/Sloe* ⊛

Prunus spinosa

(Rose Family)

Spiny deciduous shrub to 5 m tall, with short-stalked, elliptic, toothed leaves. Flowers white, opening on short stalks close to twigs, before the leaves appear, often brightening entire hedgerows in early spring. Sepals 2 mm long. Flowers about 1–1.5 cm across. Stamens 20. Fruit a rounded, sour-tasting drupe, 1–1.5 cm across, black, with bluish bloom when ripe.

Flowering season: Mar–Apr

Habitat: Woodland edges, hedgerows, scrub, rocky sites.

Distribution: Europe; W Asia; N Africa.

Active ingredients: Coumarin derivatives, some prussic acid-glycosides, flavone-glycosides.

Uses: Tea is mild laxative; leaves yield a mouthwash.

Further uses: The ripe berries are used to flavour drinks including sloe gin.

Home use tips: A laxative tea. Boil 2 teaspoonful in 250 ml water. 2 cups daily.

181 182 Common Hawthorn* ✿   *Crataegus monogyna*

(Rose Family)

Variable shrub or small tree growing to about 10 m tall, with short woody spines 1–2.5 cm long. Leaves alternate, broadly oval or diamond shaped, 3–6 cm long, with 3–7 deep, pointed lobes; lobes toothed towards tip; tufts of hairs in vein angles. Flowers white, long-stalked, in dense clusters. Individual flowers 8–15 mm across, 5-partite, usually with a single style. Sepals triangular, later turning back. Stamens 20. Fruits (below left), known as haws, oval or round, 7–10 mm long, single-seeded, red.

Flowering season: May–June

Habitat: Woodland, hedgerows, scrub; gardens.

Distribution: Most of Europe; N Africa.

Active ingredients: Flowers: tannins, flavonoids, essential oil, triterpene-carbonic acids, purine derivatives. Fruits: tannins, flavonoids, pigments, vitamins.

Uses: To treat various heart and circulatory problems and to support Digitalis therapy.

Further uses: Young leaves are good in salads. Haws make good wine, jelly, and add flavour to brandy.

Home use tips: To treat nervous heart problems. Infuse 2 teaspoonful flowers in 250 ml boiling hot water for 20 minutes. Drink 2–3 cups daily.

183 Midland Hawthorn* ✿   *Crataegus laevigata*

(Rose Family)

Shrub or small tree growing to about 10 m tall. Resembles previous species, but has less spiny twigs, less deeply cut leaves, with 3(5) more or less blunt lobes, with irregular teeth. Lacks tufts of hairs in vein angles. Flowers slightly larger, mostly with 2 styles (more rarely 1 or 3). Fruit to 12 mm, mostly 2-stoned.

Flowering season: May–June

Habitat: Woodland, hedgerows, scrub; more shade-tolerant than previous species.

Distribution: Europe, except eastern part; in BI only common in lowland England.

Active ingredients and uses: See Common Hawthorn.

Note: The variety Paul's Scarlet is a pink-flowered garden variety of this species. Hybrids between Common and Midland Hawthorn are quite frequent.

Rowan/Mountain Ash* ✿

Sorbus aucuparia

(Rose Family)

Fast-growing deciduous tree to 15(20) m, with loose, rounded
crown and pale grey, smooth bark. Young shoots downy, later hairless.
Leaves alternate, stalked, pinnate, 10–20 cm long, with 9–17 narrowly
elliptical, pointed leaflets, each 2–6 cm long and coarsely toothed.
Grey-green below, hairy or smooth; dark red or yellow in autumn. Leaf
stalk furrowed and hairy. Flowers white, to about 1 cm across, with 5 petals,
normally 3-styled; in large clusters, to about 15 cm across. Sepals triangular,
1.5 mm long, with glandular hairs. Petals oval or round, 4–5 mm long.
Stamens 20, about the same length as petals. Normally 3 styles. Fruit small
and rounded, 9–10 mm broad, usually containing 3 seeds. Yellow, ripening
to orange-red.

Flowering season: May–July

Habitat: Open woodland; upland areas, wooded bog. Commonly planted as
a decorative tree.

Distribution: Most of Europe; W Siberia.

Active ingredients: Tannins, sorbic and parasorbic acids, vitamin C, sugar,
pectin.

Uses: Bark and leaves used as a gargle against thrush, and the berries as
gargle for sore throat.

Further uses: Berries, especially of the sweet form var. *moravica*, used in
tarts and jellies, or to make wine.

Home use tips: To stimulate the appetite. Eat 1 teaspoonful rowan jam daily.

Quince* ✿

Cydonia oblonga

(Rose Family)

Spineless shrub or tree to 8 m tall. Young growth downy at first,
yellow-green. Leaves alternate. Stalk 1–2 cm long, with felty hairs; blade
ovate to broadly elliptic, 5–10 cm long, with entire margins, and felty grey
hairs below. Stipules at base of leaf-stalk obovate, 6–12 mm long, hairy
beneath. Flowers white or pale pink, solitary, 3–5 cm across. Sepals 5, 8–15
mm long, downy, persisting into fruit. Styles 5. Fruit large, pale yellow,
apple- or pear-shaped, softly hairy and aromatic, crowned by calyx.

Flowering season: May–June

Habitat: Sunny slopes, woodland margins. Also planted.

Distribution: Asia. Cultivated in Europe, especially in C and S, sometimes
naturalised. In BI, introduced and scattered; sometimes found in hedges
and woods, mainly in the south.

Active ingredients: Mucilage, amygdalin (a prussic acid-glycoside), tannin,
fatty oil.

Uses: To treat constipation and coughs. Externally for burns, chapped skin
and haemorrhoids.

Further uses: As a constituent of cosmetics. Fruits for jelly and jam and as
flavouring for apple pies and liqueurs.

188 Fenugreek* ✻

(Pea Family)

Trigonella foenum-graecum

Almost hairless annual, to 50 cm, with branching stem. Leaves trifoliate, with obovate to lanceolate leaflets to 3 cm long. Flowers yellowish-white, singly or in pairs, in leaf axils. Calyx tubular, with 5 narrow, hairy teeth. Corolla 0.8–1.8 cm long, wings and keel much shorter than standard. Fruit a long pod, to 10 cm long and 1 cm wide. Seeds flat, yellow-brown.
Flowering season: May–July
Habitat: Dry grassland, waste ground; cultivated.
Distribution: E Mediterranean; Asia. In BI introduced casual, mainly in south.
Active ingredients: Mucilage, protein, fatty and essential oils, saponin, trigonellin (alkaloid).
Uses: To treat boils and skin infections. Seed tea relieves digestive and menstrual pain. Research has revealed that it can reduce blood cholesterol.
Further uses: Seeds as flavourings for curries and chutneys. Sprouted seeds added to salads.
Home use tips: On a poultice to treat boils and skin infections. Boil 100 g ground seeds to a paste.

189 Goat's Rue* ✻

(Pea Family)

Galega officinalis

Hairless or sparsely hairy perennial to 1.5 m. Leaves pinnate, with 9–17 elliptic or ovate leaflets each about 4 cm long. Flowers white or bluish-mauve, in erect racemes. Calyx bell-shaped, 5-partite. Fruit a pod about 2–3 cm long and 2–3 mm wide.
Flowering season: July–Sep
Habitat: Waste ground, tips; gardens.
Distribution: S Europe; Asia. In BI introduced casual, mainly in south.
Active ingredients: Alkaloids, saponins, flavone-glycosides.
Uses: Occasionally in treatment of diabetes. Diuretic and fever-reducing. Also to expel worms. Tea from flowers is an antibiotic, and also stimulates milk production (in women and livestock).
Further uses: Fresh juice used to clot milk in cheese making.

190 French Bean* ✻

(Pea Family)

Phaseolus vulgaris

Bushy or climbing annual to 4 m. Leaves long-stalked, with 3 leaflets each 5–20 cm long. Inflorescence short-stalked, with 2–6 white, sometimes purplish long-stalked flowers, each 1–1.5 cm long. Calyx bell-shaped with 5 unequal teeth. Fruit a pod, 10–20 cm long with large seeds.
Flowering season: June–Sep
Habitat: Waste ground, tips; gardens.
Distribution: S America. In BI introduced casual, mainly in south.
Active ingredients: Trigonellin, amino acids, glucokinine.
Uses: Diuretic. Pods improve high blood pressure and regulate sugar metabolism.
Home use tips: A diuretic tea for treating urinary problems. Boil 1 dessertspoon of bean husks in 250 ml water for 3 minutes. Drink 1 cup 2–3 times daily.
Similar species: Runner Bean* ✻ (*P. coccineus*) is similar but climbs more and has red flowers. Introduced garden plant, from tropical America.

191   Lemon ✿

Citrus limon

(Rue Family)

Evergreen broad-leaved tree to 10 m tall, with rounded crown. Stems with spines in the leaf axils. Leaves to 16 cm long, alternate, with scarcely winged stalk, leathery, elliptic, pointed, shiny dark green above and finely toothed. Flowers white, often suffused pink on outside, singly or in small groups in leaf axils. Sepals 4–5, short. Petals 5. Stamens 25–40. Fruit the familiar lemon, 7–15 cm long, yellow, rough, with sour flesh.

Flowering season: Mar–Sep

Habitat: Well-drained soils, in areas with Mediterranean climate.

Distribution: Unknown in the wild, probably originated in eastern Himalaya. Grown in Mediterranean region and many subtropical countries. Also occasionally elsewhere, under glass. Cannot be grown outside in BI.

Active ingredients: Essential oils, coumarin derivatives, hesperidine and other flavonoids, bitters.

Uses: Juice is antiseptic and astringent. The pure isolated flavonoids, notably hesperidine, are used to treat certain venous disorders and flu.

Further uses: Fruit, juice and peel used widely as a constituent and flavouring for drinks. Juice in salad dressing. Essential oils used as perfume in cosmetics and scents.

Home use tips: Tea to stimulate the appetite. Infuse 1 teaspoonful of equal amounts of lemon peel, Centaury and rosehips in 250 ml boiling hot water for 5 minutes. Drink 1 cup, half an hour before each meal.

192   Bitter/Seville/Sour Orange ✿

Citrus aurantium

(Rue Family)

Evergreen broad-leaved tree to 12 m tall. Twigs carry rather thin thorns. Leaves alternate, leathery, stalked, 7.7–10 cm long, broadly elliptic and entire. Leaf stalk winged. Flowers white, very fragrant, singly or in small groups in leaf axils. Sepals 4–5, short. Petals 5. Stamens 20. Fruit an orange, rounded, 7–8 cm across, with thick rind and sour flesh.

Flowering season: Mar–May

Habitat: Well-drained soils, in areas with Mediterranean climate.

Distribution: Probably originated in SE Asia. Brought to Europe in 10th century by Arabs. Grown in Mediterranean region, mainly in Spain.

Active ingredients: Essential oils, hesperidine and other flavonoids, bitters.

Uses: To stimulate the appetite and aid digestion. Leaves and shoots yield petit-grain oil used to treat anxiety. Seed oil reduces cholesterol.

Further uses: To make marmalade. Flowers yield Neroli oil, used in perfumes and aromatherapy.

Home use tips: Tea to stimulate the appetite. Infuse 1 teaspoonful of equal amounts of bitter orange peel, Centaury and rosehips in 250 ml boiling hot water for 5 minutes. Drink 1 cup, half an hour before each meal.

191

192

Horse Chestnut* ⊛

Aesculus hippocastanum

(Horse Chestnut Family)

Deciduous tree growing to over 30 m tall, with a broad, dense crown and
smooth, later grey-brown and scaly bark. Young shoots with soft, brown
hairs. Winter buds large, shiny, reddish-brown and sticky. Leaves opposite,
long-stalked, palmate, with 5–7 long, obovate leaflets radiating from a
central point; turning yellow in the autumn. Leaflets to about 25 cm long,
double-toothed at margins, dark green above, paler green below. Flowers
in large (20–30 cm) upright, many-flowered panicles. Calyx unevenly
5-lobed. Petals 10–15 mm long, white with a yellow or pink blotch.
Stamens usually 7, long and curved. Fruit a round green prickly capsule, to
6 cm across. Seeds (1–3) large, shiny, dark brown 'conkers'.

Flowering season: May

Habitat: Shady, damp, mountain woodland (where wild). Rough ground,
copses. Widely planted.

Distribution: Balkans, (Albania, N Greece, Bulgaria); introduced elsewhere
in Europe. Naturalised in some places.

Active ingredients: Saponins, notably aescin, flavone-glycosides, tannins.

Uses: In many preparations in conventional and homeopathic medicine to
treat circulatory disorders, varicose veins, haemorrhoids, blocked veins and
frost damage. Used formerly as a tea and tincture. Bark yields a tonic for
fevers.

Further uses: Seed extract used in bath oils to improve the skin. Bark
produces a yellow dye.

White Bryony* ☠

Bryonia dioica

(Cucumber Family)

Climbing plant with tuberous root, and rough stems up to 4 m long,
climbing by means of tendrils. Leaves short-stalked, heart-shaped or
5-lobed and roughly hairy. Male and female plants separate. Flowers
greenish-white. Male flowers in long-stalked racemes, rather
funnel-shaped, up to 1 cm across. Stamens 5, of which 2 pairs fused, 1 free.
Female flowers in short-stalked umbel-like clusters. Calyx 5-lobed, 6 mm
long. Corolla funnel-shaped, deeply 5-lobed, to 2 cm across, with rounded
inferior ovary. Fruit a round, red berry, 6–7 mm across.

Flowering season: June–Sep

Habitat: Hedges, wet woods, woodland edges, waste ground, fences.

Distribution: W and C Europe. Common in lowland England; not native in
Scotland or Ireland.

Active ingredients: Resin, bitters, alkaloids.

Uses: Occasionally used in conjunction with other drugs. In homeopathy
mainly to treat rheumatism and gout.

NB: Poisonous. Do not use or prepare.

196 Myrtle ✿

Myrtus communis

(Myrtle Family)

Dense evergreen shrub to about 3 m tall. Stems rectangular, and downy when young. Leaves 1–3 cm long, opposite, sessile, oval to lanceolate, pointed and entire; leathery and shiny, with obvious midrib. Flowers fragrant, white, to 3 cm across, with glandular stalk, solitary in leaf axils. Sepals 5, triangular, at first upright, later curving back. Petals 5, obovate, glandular. Stamens numerous, as long as petals, with yellow anthers. Fruit a round or oval pea-sized blue-black berry.

Flowering season: June–Sep

Habitat: Dry, rocky slopes, maquis.

Distribution: Mediterranean; N Africa.

Active ingredients: Essential oils including cineol, myrtenol; terpenes, bitters, tannins.

Uses: As expectorant in bronchitis and lung complaints. In homeopathy for tuberculosis and persistent coughs. Myrtol used for gingivitis. Leaves are antiseptic and astringent; decoction used for haemorrhoids and bruises.

Further uses: Flowers a constituent of toilet water and dried in pot-pourri and herb pillows. Leaves used to flavour roast meat, and buds and berries in sweets.

197 198 Alder Buckthorn *

Frangula alnus

(Buckthorn Family)

Deciduous non-spiny shrub to 3 m tall, with smooth bark. Leaves to 5 cm long, alternate, entire, with 6–10 pairs of lateral veins. Flowers 5-partite, greenish white, long-stalked, in clusters of 2–10. Calyx funnel-shaped, 5-lobed, 6 mm long. Petals slightly shorter, enclosing 5 stamens. Fruit a round berry, about 8 mm across, green, ripening through red to black.

Flowering season: May–June

Habitat: Damp woods, scrub, bogs, fens.

Distribution: Most of Europe; Turkey; Caucasus.

Active ingredients: Bark: anthrone (when fresh), turning to anthraquinone on storage, tannins, bitters, saponin.

Uses: Mild laxative.

Home use tips: Mild laxative infusion. 1 teaspoonful commercially produced bark extract in 250 ml cold water for 12 hours. Drink 1 cup (lukewarm) last thing at night.

NB: Use only commercial preparations, as fresh plant can be poisonous.

196

199 ## Field Eryngo* ☒   *Eryngium campestre*
(Carrot Family)

Hairless, thorny perennial, to 1 m tall, with robust, branching stem. Leaves tough and stiff, whitish-green. Basal leaves long-stalked, pinnate and spiny; upper leaves short-stalked or sessile, upper ones finely divided. Flowers in rounded or oval terminal heads, to 15 cm across, with linear-lanceolate spiny bracts below. Spiny scales sticking out between the flowers. Sepals 5, lanceolate and spiny, about 2 mm long. Petals whitish, about 1 mm long.

Flowering season: July–Sep

Habitat: Dry grassland and rough places, often near the sea; also vineyards, open woods.

Distribution: Mainly C and S Europe, north to Germany and Holland; W Asia. In BI, rare plant in S and SW Britain.

Active ingredients: Essential oil, saponins, tannins.

Uses: In certain preparations as an infusion to treat coughs, whooping cough, and urinary infections.

Similar species: Sea Holly* ☒ (*E. maritimum*) is somewhat smaller, with waxy, lobed leaves, and pale blue flowers. Found on sand and shingle on coasts of Europe, N to S Norway. N Africa; in BI, common round coasts, except in N and E Scotland. Roots were formerly candied as the sweets eryngoes, or boiled or roasted as a vegetable.

NB: Sea Holly now too rare to be dug up. Do not collect.

200 ## Sanicle*   *Sanicula europaea*
(Carrot Family)

Hairless perennial to 50 cm tall, with erect stems. Leaves mostly basal, long-stalked and palmately 5-lobed, with rough, toothed margins. Stem leaves small, unstalked. Flower clusters arranged in small umbels, with the side branches generally in groups of 3; surrounded by 4–8 involucral bracts. Outer flowers male, many; inner flowers female, 1–3. Sepals 5, about 1 mm long. Petals 5, whitish, about 1.5 mm long. Fruit rounded and bristly.

Flowering season: May–June

Habitat: Mixed deciduous woods, beech woods; calcareous soils.

Distribution: Europe, W Asia.

Active ingredients: Essential oil, saponins, tannins, bitters, allantoin.

Uses: In homeopathy to treat stomach and intestinal problems. Also as a gargle for sore throats or in compress for bruises or skin rashes.

Home use tips: As a tea for throat infections. Infuse 2 teaspoonsful in 250 ml boiling hot water for 10 minutes. Drink 2 cups daily. Externally as a gargle or for use on compress or poultice.

NB: Danger of confusion with other (poisonous) umbellifers, therefore do not collect; use only bought preparations.

Note: **The name comes from 'sana', meaning healthy in Latin.**

199

200

201 ## Ground-elder*   *Aegopodium podagraria*

(Carrot Family)

Hairless perennial to 1 m tall, with thin, creeping stolons; often covering
large areas. Stem hollow, ridged and branching towards the top. Leaves
once- to twice-ternate, with finely toothed lobes. Lower leaves stalked;
upper leaves with inflated sheathing base. Flowers white, in umbels of
15–25 spokes, without bracts. Petals about 1.5 mm long, with 2-lobed tip.
Fruit brown; oval with fan-like ridges.

Flowering season: June–Aug

Habitat: Wet woodland, river banks, hedges, gardens; often a persistent
garden weed.

Distribution: Most of Europe; Turkey; N Asia.

Active ingredients: Essential oils.

Uses: In homeopathy to treat rheumatism and gout.

Further uses: The leaves make a good, spinach-like vegetable. Eaten by the
Romans, and still a common pot-herb in Scandinavia.

202 ## Caraway* ⊛   *Carum carvi*

(Carrot Family)

Hairless biennial or perennial to 1 m tall with ridged stem often branched
from base. Leaves rather feathery, 2- to 3-pinnate with narrow, pointed
segments. Lower leaves stalked; upper leaves unstalked. Umbels with 8–16
spokes. Bracts and bracteoles usually absent. Flowers white or pinkish and
1.5 mm long. Fruit 3–4 mm long, elliptical, brown with pale ribs, aromatic
when crushed.

Flowering season: May–July

Habitat: Hay meadows, pasture (especially upland), footpaths; cultivated as
herb.

Distribution: Most of Europe (only in upland areas in S); N Africa; Asia. In
BI, introduced, scattered, mainly in SE England.

Active ingredients: Essential oil, notably carvon.

Uses: To treat loss of appetite and digestive disorders. Seeds are antiseptic
and help dispel worms.

Further uses: As herb or spice, particularly in C European cuisine (such as
sauerkraut, goulash, and in cheeses, pickles and rye bread and cakes).
Young stems and leaves may be added to soups and salads and the root
cooked as vegetable. Seed-oil flavours the liqueur Kümmel; also cosmetics
and soap.

Home use tips: As a tea for loss of appetite, digestive disorders and
flatulence. Infuse 1 teaspoonful crushed fruits ('seeds') in 250 ml boiling
hot water for 10 minutes. Drink 3 cups daily.

**NB: Danger of confusion with other (poisonous) umbellifers,
therefore do not collect; use only bought preparations.**

201

202

203 Aniseed/Anise ✳   *Pimpinella anisum*

(Carrot Family)

Softly hairy annual to 50 cm tall, with branched stem. Lower leaves long-stalked, rounded and toothed; upper leaves lobed. Flowers white, in umbels with 5–15 spokes. Bracts absent. Petals 1.5 mm long, hairy. Fruit oval, slightly flattened, 3–4 mm long, with characteristic aniseed aroma.

Flowering season: July–Aug

Habitat: Dry, warm sites; also planted.

Distribution: C and S Europe; Russia; Egypt.

Active ingredients: Essential oil, notably anethol.

Uses: To treat coughs, digestive disorders and flatulence. Also encourages breast milk, and said to ease childbirth.

Further uses: Fruits ('seeds') as herb and spice, and in drinks such as ouzo and Pernod. Young leaves added to salads, and stems and roots to soups.

Home use tips: As a tea for coughs, loss of appetite, digestive disorders and flatulence; externally as a gargle for throat infection. Infuse 1 teaspoonful crushed fruits ('seeds') (mixed with equal proportions of Fennel and Caraway) in 250 ml boiling hot water for 10 minutes. Drink 2–5 cups daily.

204 Greater Burnet-saxifrage*   *Pimpinella major*

(Carrot Family)

Hairless or slightly hairy perennial to 1 m tall, with hollow, furrowed stem. Leaves shiny, pinnate, with unevenly toothed lobes. Inflorescence an umbel with 9–15 spokes. Bracts absent. Flowers white or pale pink. Petals 1–1.5 mm long. Fruit oval, hairless, 3–4 mm.

Flowering season: June–Aug

Habitat: Rich meadows, tall-herb communities, woodland edges.

Distribution: Most of Europe, except for far W and N. In BI, locally common in E England and SW Ireland; elsewhere local and rare.

Active ingredients: Essential oil, saponin, tannins, bitters.

Uses: To treat coughs and digestive disorders.

205 Burnet-saxifrage*   *Pimpinella saxifraga*

(Carrot Family)

Perennial to about 70 cm tall. Resembles previous species, but has solid, finely-ribbed stem, and narrower leaflets. Fruit broadly oval to rounded, 2–2.5 mm.

Flowering season: July–Oct

Habitat: Dry grassland and rocky sites.

Distribution: Most of Europe.

Active ingredients and uses: See Greater Burnet-saxifrage (204).

203

204
205

206 Hemlock* ☠

Conium maculatum

(Carrot Family)

Hairless biennial to 2 m tall, with feathery foliage and unpleasant mousy smell. Stem hollow, ridged, with purple-brown spots and a bluish bloom; much-branched. Leaves 2–4-pinnate. Lower leaves up to 50 cm long and 40 cm across; upper leaves smaller. Flowers in umbels with 10–15 spokes and several linear bracts. Petals 1.5 mm long. Fruit oval, 2.5–3.5 mm long, with wavy ridges.

Flowering season: July–Sep

Habitat: Roadsides, ditches, waste ground.

Distribution: Europe; N Asia. In BI common everywhere except W and C Scotland.

Active ingredients: Alkaloids, notably coniine, essential oil, bitters, flavone-glycosides.

Uses: Formerly to treat neurological disorders. In homeopathy to treat dizziness, swollen glands, certain eye conditions, thickened arteries and prostate problems.

NB: Deadly poisonous and confusable with other, harmless umbellifers. Therefore only bought medicines should be used for all members of this family.

Note: The Ancient Greeks used a decoction of Hemlock as a means of execution; it is sedative and anaesthetic, and fatal. Socrates killed himself by drinking Hemlock.

207 Coriander* ☺

Coriandrum sativum

(Carrot Family)

Hairless aromatic annual to 50 cm tall. Stem round and branching towards the top. Leaves pale green. Basal leaves stalked, simple, with 3 or more wide lobes; stem leaves 2–3 pinnate, with linear lobes. Flowers white or pinkish, in flat-topped, 3–5 spoked umbels. Calyx with 5 lanceolate lobes. Fruit round, 2–6 mm across, pale brown.

Flowering season: June–July

Habitat: Sunny sites. Waste ground, tips.

Distribution: E Mediterranean. In BI, introduced and casual.

Active ingredients: Essential oil, bitters, tannins.

Uses: Oil used medicinally to treat rheumatism. Seed is a mild sedative, eases migraine and flatulence and aids digestion.

Further uses: As herb or spice. Fruits ('seeds') and fresh root used in curries. Leaves used in middle eastern cuisine. Seed oil used in perfume and incense, in massage oil, and to flavour toothpaste.

Home use tips: As a tea for digestive disorders and flatulence (best if mixed with equal proportions of Caraway, Fennel and Aniseed). Infuse 2 teaspoonsful of mixture in 250 ml boiling hot water for 10 minutes. Drink 3 cups daily.

206

207

Wild Celery* ☒

Apium graveolens

(Carrot Family)

Hairless biennial, growing to 1 m tall, with spindle-shaped tap-root, and branching grooved stems. The whole plant smells of celery. Leaves dark green, shiny. Lower leaves long-stalked, 1- or 2-pinnate, with toothed, mainly 3-lobed leaflets. Flowers (top right) creamy white or greenish, in numerous small 6–12 spoked umbels. Bracts absent. Petals only about 0.5 mm long. Fruit 1.5–2 mm, laterally compressed, with slender ridges.

Flowering season: June–Oct

Habitat: Saltmarshes, swampy areas, ditches.

Distribution: Europe; W Asia. In BI rather local; mainly coastal.

Active ingredients: Essential oil, apiine (a flavone-glycoside).

Uses: Aids digestion. Seed-oil clears toxins and reduces swelling; helpful in arthritis and gout.

Further uses: Leaves can be eaten cooked in stews (mildly toxic when fresh). Seeds can be added to pickles and curry.

Home use tips: As a diuretic in cases of bladder or kidney problems. Boil 2 teaspoonsful in 250 ml water. Drink 2 cups daily.

NB: Use only cultivated forms, because the wild plant is rather local, and mildly toxic when fresh. There is also a risk of confusion with poisonous relatives.

Note: Cultivated Celery ⊛ is var. *dulce*. This is grown for its fat, edible leaf stalks. Celeriac ⊛ is var. *rapaceum*. It produces swollen stem-bases and is eaten as a vegetable.

Spignel/Baldmoney*

Meum athamanticum

(Carrot Family)

Hairless perennial with hollow stem; sweetly aromatic. Stem simple or somewhat branched, mainly leafless, surrounded at base by remains of previous season's leaves. Leaves nearly all basal, long-stalked, 2- to 4-pinnate and feathery. Flowers white or pinkish, in umbels with 6–15 spokes. Bracts lacking or few; bracteoles 3–8. Petals 1.5 mm long. Fruit 6–10 mm long, brown, with 5 longitudinal ridges.

Flowering season: May–Aug

Habitat: Mountain grassland.

Distribution: W and C Europe. In BI, mainly in N Britain and S and C Scotland.

Active ingredients: Essential oil, resin, gum, starch, sugar, fatty oil.

Uses: Earlier used medicinally as appetite stimulant and to aid digestion.

Further uses: A constituent of a digestive schnapps.

NB: Danger of confusion with other (poisonous) umbellifers, therefore do not collect or use from wild.

211 # Masterwort*   *Peucedanum (Imperatoria) ostruthium*

(Carrot Family)

Hairless perennial to 1 m tall, with hollow, branching stems. Leaves
1–2-ternate, with elliptical to lanceolate, toothed segments. Lower leaves
long-stalked, to 30 cm long; upper leaves sessile, with inflated sheaths.
Flowers white, in large, flat umbels with up to 50 spokes. Bracts usually
absent; bracteoles few and bristle-like. Petals 1–1.5 mm long, broadly
obovate. Fruit almost spherical, winged, 4–5 mm long, with 3 longitudinal
ridges.

Flowering season: June–Aug

Habitat: Marshy fields, riversides, tall-herb communities, green alder
scrub; upland.

Distribution: European mountains. In BI, mainly in the north.

Active ingredients: Essential oil, bitters, tannins.

Uses: Appetite stimulant and aid to digestion. To treat bronchitis.

Home use tips: Digestive tea: Boil 2 teaspoonful in 250 ml water for
2 minutes. Drink 2–3 cups daily. To inhale for bronchitis; put 2 dessert-
spoonful in 250 ml boiling water. Inhale the steam for 10 minutes.

**NB: Danger of confusion with other (poisonous) umbellifers,
therefore do not collect or use from wild, and use only bought
preparations.**

212 # Wild Angelica*   *Angelica sylvestris*

(Carrot Family)

Hairless perennial to 2 m tall, with hollow, rounded, branching, somewhat
purplish stem. Leaves large, twice-pinnate, with elliptic, toothed lobes.
Lower leaves to 60 cm long, long-stalked; stem leaves sessile, with inflated
sheaths. Flowers white or pinkish, in large, convex, 20–40-spoked umbels.
Bracts lacking or 1–3, soon falling; bracteoles numerous, very narrow.
Petals 1–1.5 mm long. Fruits oval and flattened, with winged edges,
4–5 mm long.

Flowering season: July–Aug

Habitat: Wet woods; damp meadows, tall-herb communities.

Distribution: Europe; Siberia.

Active ingredients: Essential oil, coumarin, furocoumarin.

Uses: Root used formerly to treat coughs and digestive disorders. In
homeopathy the fruits are used to treat nervous fatigue and nervous
digestive problems.

211

212

Bearberry* ☒
Arctostaphylos uva-ursi

(Heath Family)

Low, many-branched, evergreen dwarf shrub, with stems to 1.5 m. Leaves tough, obovate, 1–3 cm long, entire; stalk about 1 mm long. Inflorescence 3–10 flowered; flowers pinkish-white. Corolla ovoid and fused, with 5 short lobes at tip; hairy inside. Fruit (centre left) a red berry, 6–8 mm across.

Flowering season: May–Aug

Habitat: Pine woods, heath, peaty heather moor.

Distribution: Europe; N Asia; N America. In BI locally common in N England, Scotland and Ireland.

Active ingredients: Arbutin, tannins, flavone-glycosides.

Uses: To treat urinary and bladder infections. The stem and leaves brewed as traditional native American cure for headache and scurvy.

Further uses: The leaves and twigs yield yellow and green dye.

Home use tips: For acute bladder infection. Infuse 2 teaspoonsful in 250 ml cold water for 12–24 hours. Drink 2–3 cups daily, lukewarm. Do not consume acid food or drink during treatment.

---

215 # Cowberry*
Vaccinium vitis-idaea

(Heath Family)

Evergreen dwarf shrub, to 30 cm tall. Leaves thick, obovate, with downrolled margin; dark green above, pale green below. Inflorescence drooping, many-flowered. Corolla bell-shaped, pinkish-white, 8–10 mm long, 5-lobed, hairless within. Fruit (centre right) a red berry, 6–10 mm across.

Flowering season: May–June

Habitat: Peaty woods, bogs, heaths.

Distribution: C and N Europe; N Asia; N America. In BI, locally common, mainly in N Britain. Scattered in Ireland.

Active ingredients: Arbutin, tannins, flavone-glycosides.

Uses: Earlier used as Bearberry.

Further uses: Fruits are edible, but not as tasty as bilberries (115/116).

---

216 # Bogbean* ✺ ☒
Menyanthes trifoliata

(Bogbean Family)

Semi-aquatic hairless perennial to 35 cm tall. Leaves long-stalked, trifoliate, with ovate leaflets. Inflorescence an erect raceme, on a leafless stalk. Calyx split almost to the base into 5 lobes. Corolla pinkish-white, with short funnel-shaped tube and 5 hairy, spreading or reflexed lobes.

Flowering season: May–June

Habitat: Fens, bogs, wet flushes, lake margins.

Distribution: Europe; Asia; N America. Throughout BI, but only local in much of England.

Active ingredients: Bitters, tannins, flavonoids.

Uses: Appetite stimulant, an aid to digestion, and to treat diarrhoea. In homeopathy to treat flu. Also thought to regularise periods.

Further uses: Used by Canadian Inuit as source of flour (from ground roots).

Home use tips: Tea for loss of appetite and diarrhoea. Boil 1 teaspoonful in 250 ml water for 1 minute. Drink 1 cup, just before meals.

NB: Protected species. Do not collect. Over-use can upset digestion.

213

214
215

216

Olive ✤

Olea europaea

(Olive Family)

Long-lived evergreen broad-leaved tree, to 15 m tall. Trunk often twisted and short, branching from quite low down, thick and knotted in old specimens. Stems rounded or square, sometimes thorny, with downy hairs when young. Leaves opposite, leathery, narrowly elliptical to lanceolate (willow-like), 4–8 cm long, with entire margins (often slightly furled). Dark or grey-green above and smooth or slightly hairy; with dense covering of silver-grey hairs beneath. Flowers small, creamy-white, in panicles in leaf axils. Calyx fused and cup-shaped, 4-toothed. Corolla white, 4-lobed, tubular. Stamens 2, arising at base of corolla tube. Ovary superior, with style and 2-branched stigma. Fruit the well-known olive; a drupe, to 4 cm long, with hard, rough stone surrounded by edible, oily flesh. At first green, ripening through pink, usually to black.

Flowering season: June

Habitat: Dry, warm, sunny sites. Usually planted on deep, rich soils.

Distribution: Mediterranean region; cultivated in many parts of the world with similar climate.

Active ingredients: Bitters, alkaloids (leaves); oil, notably glycerides of oleic acid.

Uses: Leaf extract used medicinally to lower blood pressure.

Further uses: Fruits eaten in Mediterranean cuisine, and to produce valuable oil (rich in unsaturated fatty acids), used for cooking and in skin-care.

Note: An important species in remnants of Mediterranean woodland and maquis in S Europe. Ancient cultivated plant (for over 4,000 years), mainly for its oil and wood.

219 Manna Ash ✤

Fraxinus ornus

(Olive Family)

Grey-barked deciduous tree growing to 20 m tall. Young twigs green, rounded or square. Leaves opposite, to 30 cm long, pinnate, with 7–9 narrowly elliptical, pointed leaflets; stalk 4–8 cm long. Undersides of leaves with rusty hairs on veins. Flowers white, scented, in upright, later drooping, panicles. Calyx very short (1 mm) fused, with 4 triangular teeth. Petals usually 4, narrow, 7–15 mm long, fused in pairs at base. Stamens 2, well overtopping ovary. Fruit a winged achene, 20–25 mm long and 4–6 mm wide; wing about the same length as achene.

Flowering season: June

Habitat: Mixed woodland, scrub.

Distribution: S Europe (north to the southern edge of the Alps); Turkey. Grown elsewhere in Europe as an ornamental tree in parks, gardens and at roadsides.

Active ingredients: Mannitol, other sugars, resin, traces of the glycoside fraxin.

Uses: Sap used as a mild laxative, especially for children.

Note: The sap hardens into a sweet gum, known as 'manna', once used as a famine food. Cultivated in S Italy and Sicily for this sugar-rich syrup which exudes from damaged stems.

220 Swallow-wort/Vincetoxicum ☠

(Milkweed Family)   *Vincetoxicum hirundinaria*

Sparsely hairy or hairless perennial to 1 m tall with unbranched stem.
Leaves opposite, short-stalked, broadly lanceolate, with rounded or
heart-shaped base, and with short hairs along veins on underside. Flowers
greenish-yellow or greenish-white, in clusters in the upper leaf axils,
surrounded by small, lanceolate bracts. Calyx lobes 2 mm long, pointed.
Corolla funnel-shaped, 4–5 mm wide and deeply 5-lobed. Fruit a long pod
to 50 mm long. Seeds 6–7 mm long, narrowly oval and flat, with white hairs
at the tip.

Flowering season: May–Aug

Habitat: Dry grassland, open woods, scrub.

Distribution: Europe, except the N and NW; Asia; N Africa.

Active ingredients: Mixture of glycosides, alkaloids, flavone-glycosides.

Uses: In homeopathy for high blood pressure and for fevers.

NB: **Very poisonous. Do not collect or prepare.**

221 Field Bindweed*

(Bindweed Family)   *Convolvulus arvensis*

Almost hairless perennial with creeping underground stems, and trailing or
climbing stems to 1 m long. Leaves alternate, long-stalked, shaped like a
spearhead, about 4 cm long, getting smaller towards stem tips. Flowers
white, or pink with pale stripes, scented, solitary in leaf axils. Calyx with
3 longer and 2 shorter lobes. Corolla funnel-shaped, 1.5–2.5 cm long. Fruit
an oval capsule, 5–8 mm long.

Flowering season: May–Sep

Habitat: Hedges, farmland, footpaths; also a garden weed.

Distribution: Widespread. In BI throughout the lowlands, but absent from
most of N Scotland.

Active ingredients: Glycosides, tannins, flavonoids.

Uses: Occasionally, with other medicines, as a laxative.

222 Hedge Bindweed*

(Bindweed Family)   *Calystegia sepium*

Climbing hairless perennial, with stems to 3 m long. Leaves alternate,
heart-shaped or arrow-shaped, pointed, stalked. Flowers white, solitary in
the leaf axils, 3.5–4 cm long, with 2 broad, lanceolate sepal-like bracts at the
base, partly obscuring calyx. Calyx 10 mm long. Corolla large and
funnel-shaped.

Flowering season: June–Sep

Habitat: Wet woods, fens, reedbeds, ditches, hedges.

Distribution: Widespread.

Active ingredients: Glycosides, tannins.

Uses: Sap extract as laxative.

Similar species: Large Bindweed* ✿ (*C. silvatica*) has inflated bracts at the
base of the flower, overlapping each other and completely enclosing the
calyx. Corolla to 7.5 cm long. Forms may have either white or pink-striped
flowers. A garden escape; native of S Europe.

Sweet Pepper* ⊛

Capsicum annuum

(Nightshade Family)

Hairless, shrubby annual, to 50 cm tall, with erect, branching stem.
Leaves alternate, 1.5–12 cm long, long-stalked, lanceolate to oval, with
pointed tip. Flowers solitary, stalked and nodding, white or greenish, in
axils of upper leaves. Calyx bell-shaped, with 5 short lobes. Corolla with
short funnel-shaped tube, opening into spreading lobes, usually 5 or 6,
each 10 mm wide. Stamens 5 or 6, with bluish anthers. Fruit is a hollow,
many-seeded berry, very variable in shape, colour and size, depending on
the cultivar; usually between 5–12 cm long and up to 10 cm thick. Green at
first, ripening to yellow, red or brownish-purple.

Flowering season: June–Sep

Habitat: Cultivated.

Distribution: Native to tropical America. Occasional casual in BI.

Active ingredients: Capsaicin (responsible for hot taste), carotenoids,
flavone-glycosides, vitamin C.

Uses: To treat loss of appetite and digestive disorders. Externally on
bandage or as tincture to treat pleurisy, rheumatism and frost-bite. In
homeopathy for throat and middle-ear infections.

Further uses: As vegetable and spice.

Note: Hundreds of varieties of this species are grown in the tropics, but
only 4 or 5 are commonly grown in Europe. These are: Sweet Peppers,
which have large mild fruits; Paprikas are long, and often pointed, with
thinner flesh and slightly sharp; Chillies are narrowly conical and hot in
flavour; Wrinkled Peppers are fairly hot, wrinkled and oval. The hottest
chillies are the fruits of a related species the Bird Chilli ⊛ (*C. frutescens*)
which has erect fruits, about 2–3 cm long, usually red when ripe.

Thorn-apple* ☠

Datura stramonium

(Nightshade Family)

Robust, usually hairless annual. Leaves large (to 20 cm), simple, coarsely
toothed or lobed and pointed, with long stalks; dark green above, paler
beneath. Flowers white or purplish, upright and stalked, solitary and
terminal, or in branch angles. Calyx tubular, to 4.5 cm long, slightly
inflated, with 5 teeth. Corolla 5.5–7.5 cm long, narrowly funnel-shaped.
Fruit an oval spiny capsule to 5 cm long, splitting almost to base into
4 valves on ripening. Seeds numerous, brownish-black, 3 mm long.

Flowering season: June–Oct

Habitat: Waste land, tips, farmyards, gardens.

Distribution: America. Introduced to Europe. Occasional casual in BI.

Active ingredients: Hyoscyamine, scopolamine, atropine (alkaloids);
flavonoids.

Uses: As anti-spasmodic to treats coughs and asthma, and Parkinson's
disease. In homeopathy to treat asthma, convulsions and neuralgia.

NB: Deadly poisonous. Do not collect or use.

226 Lemon Balm* ⊛

Melissa officinalis

(Mint Family)

Lemon-scented perennial, growing to 80 cm tall. Leaves opposite, stalked, oval and toothed. Flowers pale yellow, in whorls of 3–6, in the axils of upper leaves. Calyx tubular, 2-lipped, 7–8 mm long. Corolla 12–15 mm long, 2-lipped; 2-lobed upper lip and 3-lobed lower lip.

Flowering season: June–Aug
Habitat: Well-drained soil; gardens, wasteland.
Distribution: S Europe. Much planted and naturalised elsewhere.
Active ingredients: Essential oil, bitters, tannins.
Uses: To treat nervous complaints of stomach, intestine and heart.
Further uses: Extracts are anti-viral and assist healing of wounds. Oil is an anti-depressant. Leaves add flavour to food and soothe insect bites.
Home use tips: Tea for nervous stomach. Infuse 2 teaspoonsful in 250 ml boiling hot water for 10 minutes. Drink 3 cups daily.

227 Sweet Basil ⊛

Ocimum basilicum

(Mint Family)

Annual or short-lived perennial with clove-scented leaves, growing to 60 cm. Leaves opposite, short-stalked, oval, entire or toothed, 3–5 cm long, often with rather puckered surface. Flowers white, usually in whorls of 6. Calyx with rounded upper lip and 4-toothed lower lip. Corolla 10–15 mm long, tubular; upper lip broad and 4-lobed, lower lip spoon-shaped.

Flowering season: June–Sep
Habitat: Planted. Grown commercially in many places, including California.
Distribution: Tropical Asia.
Active ingredients: Essential oil, tannins, saponin.
Uses: To treat constipation, stomach problems and flatulence.
Further uses: Culinary herb, especially with tomato, garlic and aubergines. Makes pesto sauce. Oil in perfumes and cosmetics. Wine made from leaves reputed to be an aphrodisiac. Used in massage oils (avoid if pregnant).
Home use tips: Tea for stomach problems and flatulence. Infuse 1–2 teaspoonsful in 250 ml boiling water for 10–15 minutes. Drink 1 cup as needed.

228 White Horehound* ☒

Marrubium vulgare

(Mint Family)

Aromatic perennial with downy stems and leaves, growing to 60 cm tall. Leaves opposite, stalked, broadly oval, 2–4 cm long, wrinkled and coarsely toothed at margin. Flowers white, short-stalked in tight, almost rounded whorls in upper leaf axils. Calyx 4–6 mm long with thick covering of stellate hairs and 10 spiny teeth, hooked when in fruit. Corolla 6–7 mm long, 2-lipped.

Flowering season: June–Aug
Habitat: Footpaths, wasteground, grassland.
Distribution: S and C Europe, north to S Sweden and S England (occasional); C Asia.
Active ingredients: Marrubiin, essential oil, tannins.
Uses: Infusion relaxes muscles. Used to treat coughs, bronchitis, croup and asthma, and as digestive tonic. Tea formerly used for eczema and shingles.
Home use tips: Infuse 2 teaspoonsful in boiling water. Drink 3–5 cups daily.

229 # White Dead-nettle*

Lamium album

(Mint Family)

Sparsely hairy perennial to 50 cm tall with a rectangular, usually unbranched stem. Leaves opposite, stalked and rounded to lanceolate, heart-shaped or rounded at the base and often sharply pointed; roughly toothed at the margins. Flowers white, unstalked, in whorled clusters of 6–16, in the axils of the upper leaves. Calyx funnel-shaped with unequal, pointed teeth. Corolla 2–2.5 cm long, with arching upper lip and 3-lobed, folded lower lip. Stamens 4, lying close under the upper lip, with brown and white anthers.

Flowering season: Apr–Aug

Habitat: Scrub, footpaths, waste ground, woodland, hedgerows.

Distribution: Most of Europe, except far N; N and E Asia. In BI throughout, but rare or local in N and W and probably only introduced in Ireland.

Active ingredients: Saponin, tannin, essential oil, mucilage, flavone-glycosides.

Uses: Decoction as blood tonic. Infusion externally for eczema, or internally to treat irregular or excessive periods, vaginal discharge and haemorrhoids.

Further uses: Young shoots and leaves may be eaten as a vegetable.

Home use tips: Internally for painful and irregular periods; externally as a wash. Boil 2 teaspoonful of flowers in 250 ml water and infuse for 5 minutes. Drink 2–3 cups daily.

230 # Gypsywort*

Lycopus europaeus

(Mint Family)

Almost hairless perennial growing to 1 m tall. Stem simple or branched. Leaves opposite, with short stalks or unstalked, lanceolate, 3–8 cm long, coarsely toothed, hairless or sparsely hairy. Flowers unstalked, in many-flowered whorls in the axils of the upper leaves. Calyx 2.5–4 mm long, bell-shaped, with 5 bristly teeth. Corolla 4–6 mm long, with pure white upper lip and 3-lobed, red-spotted lower lip. Stamens 2, protruding from flower.

Flowering season: July–Sep

Habitat: Reedbeds, ditches, overgrown pond margins.

Distribution: Most of Europe; N Asia. In BI throughout lowlands, but more scattered in N Scotland and Ireland.

Active ingredients: Bitters, tannins, essential oil, flavone-glycosides.

Uses: To treat slightly overactive thyroid, and nervous heart conditions.

Further uses: Juice yields a dark dye, once used by gypsies to tan their skin (hence the common name).

231 Gratiole ☠☒

Gratiola officinalis

(Figwort Family)

Hairless perennial with erect, branching stem, growing to 40 cm tall. Leaves opposite, lanceolate and pointed, unstalked and finely toothed, with 3 longitudinal veins; with glandular hairs on both surfaces. Flowers white, tinged with pink or purple, solitary and stalked, in the axils of upper leaves. Calyx with 5 long, narrow teeth. Corolla 8–10 mm long, 2-lipped, with tubular base; upper lip curving back and notched, lower lip 3-lobed. Stamens 2. Fruit a round or oval 4-chambered capsule.

Flowering season: June–Aug

Habitat: Marshy meadows, margins of rivers and ponds, ditches.

Distribution: S and C Europe, north to Holland and Germany; N and W Asia; N America.

Active ingredients: Cardiac glycosides, bitters, tannins, essential oil.

Uses: Earlier as strong laxative, but now considered too dangerous. In homeopathy to treat diarrhoea and stomach and intestinal problems.

NB: Poisonous, with similar effects to those of Foxglove (142/143). Do not use.

232 Eyebright*

Euphrasia

(Figwort Family)

Small annuals growing to about 30 cm tall. Stem usually branched towards base. Leaves sessile, oval and toothed. Flowers usually white, with a yellow throat and purplish lines; solitary, in axils of upper leaves. Calyx 5–6 mm long, 4-toothed. Corolla 8–14 mm long, enlarging during season and projecting beyond calyx, with a large, 3-lobed lower lip and a smaller upper lip which is bent backwards. Fruit a 4–6 mm long hairy capsule.

Flowering season: May–Oct

Habitat: Grassland, pasture, open woods, dunes, heath.

Distribution: Various species are found throughout Europe.

Active ingredients: Aucubin (a glycoside), tannins, bitters, essential oil.

Uses: In homeopathy internally and externally to treat eye infections and eye strain; also for coughs, colds, rheumatism and gout, and to ease hay-fever and sinusitis.

Home use tips: For eye infections such as conjunctivitis or tired eyes; internally and externally. Boil 1–2 teaspoonsful in 250 ml water, infuse for 2 minutes. Drink 1 cup, gradually over a day.

Note: The eyebrights are a difficult group to identify. There are about 30 species in the region, but only expert botanists can distinguish them reliably. One of the commonest in BI is *E. nemorosa*, which has rather large flowers, but no glandular hairs. The species illustrated is another large-flowered eyebright, with glandular hairs, *E. rostkoviana*, widespread in Europe, but rather local in BI.

231

232

Elder*

Sambucus nigra

(Honeysuckle Family)

Deciduous shrub or small tree to about 10 m tall, with rather twisted growth, and arching branches. Leaves opposite, stalked, pinnate, with 5–7 oval, elliptical, pointed leaflets with toothed margins. Foliage has characteristic, rather unpleasant smell. Flowers creamy-white and fragrant, in many-flowered, rather flat-topped clusters. Calyx tubular, with 5 short teeth. Flowers 5-partite, 6–10 mm across. Stamens 5, with yellow anthers. Fruit a berry (technically a drupe), 5–6 mm across, at first red, ripening to black; edible.

Flowering season: June–July

Habitat: Woods, hedgerows, waste ground, gardens; especially on rich soils.

Distribution: Most of Europe; W Siberia; Caucasus; Turkey.

Active ingredients: Flowers: essential oil, flavonoids, tannins, cyano-glycosides, organic acids. Fruits: organic acids, notably viburnic acid, sugar, tannins, anthocyanin, vitamins, including vitamin C.

Uses: In homeopathy to treat fevers. Cordial used for colds, coughs and bronchitis. Flowers treat hay fever and arthritis, and are a mild laxative. Leaves help bruises and sprains; bark to treat epilepsy; roots for kidney problems.

Further uses: Elderflower water is said to aid the complexion. Flowers and fruits also make wine and flowers are tasty as fritters. The buds, when pickled, are a caper substitute. The leaves are insecticidal. Plant yields black, green and violet dyes.

Home use tips: To induce sweating in cases of feverish colds. Infuse 2 teaspoonsful of flowers in 250 ml boiling hot water for 10 minutes. Drink 2 cups (hot). The vitamin-rich fruits are good for colds, either in fruit salad or as juice.

Similar species: Red-berried Elder* (*S. racemosa*) grows to about 4 m. It has a more rounded inflorescence, and its ripe fruit is bright red. In BI, introduced and naturalised, mainly in N Britain.

Dwarf Elder*

Sambucus ebulus

(Honeysuckle Family)

Almost hairless, rhizomatous perennial with erect simple stems, dying back in the autumn. Entire plant with unpleasant smell. Leaves opposite, stalked, pinnate, with 5–9 lanceolate, pointed, toothed leaflets. Stipules conspicuous, narrowly ovate and toothed. Flowers white, sometimes pinkish, smelling of bitter almonds, in many-flowered, rather domed clusters. Calyx short and 5-lobed. Corolla 6–8 mm across, 5-lobed. Stamens 5, with purple anthers. Fruit a rounded drupe ('berry'), shiny black when ripe.

Flowering season: June–Aug

Habitat: Damp woodland margins, clearings, hedges, waysides.

Distribution: C and S Europe; N Africa; W Asia. In BI scattered, possibly native.

Active ingredients: Bitters, saponins, tannin.

Uses: Medicinal preparation as a diuretic, and to reduce fluid retention.

236 Woodruff* ☠

(Bedstraw Family)

Galium odoratum

Hairless perennial to 30 cm tall, with upright, rectangular stem. Leaves in whorls of 6–9, lanceolate, with obvious midrib. Foliage smelling of new-mown hay when dried (coumarin). Flowers clustered and terminal or in the axils of the upper leaves. Calyx lacking. Corolla 4–6 mm wide, funnel-shaped with a 1 mm long tube and 4 spreading lobes. Fruit nut-like and rounded, 2–3 mm long, with hooked bristles.

Flowering season: Apr–May

Habitat: Calcareous woods, hedgerows.

Distribution: Most of Europe; N Asia.

Active ingredients: Coumarin glycoside, releasing coumarin on drying, asperuloside, tannins, bitters.

Uses: In medical preparations to treat venous and circulatory disorders.

Further uses: Dry foliage deters insects.

Note: Used traditionally in herbal medicine, but can cause internal bleeding, especially in the stomach. Added to German May Bowl Punch, but this use is now also discouraged.

237 Daisy*

(Daisy Family)

Bellis perennis

Low-growing perennial, with flowering stems to 15 cm tall. Leaves spoon-shaped, weakly toothed and stalked, growing in a basal rosette. Stem leafless and single-headed. Flowerheads 10–20 mm across. Tube florets yellow; ray florets white or pink. Fruit a simple smooth achene, about 1 mm long.

Flowering season: Mar–Nov

Habitat: Short grassland, common in garden lawns.

Distribution: Europe; Turkey; widely naturalised.

Active ingredients: Saponins, tannin, bitters, essential oil, inulin.

Uses: In homeopathy to treat sprains, bruises, boils and eczema.

Further uses: Fresh young leaves and white petals can be added to salads.

236

237

238 Feverfew* ✿ ⊕   *Tanacetum parthenium*
(Daisy Family)
Very aromatic perennial with a characteristic smell, growing to about 60 cm.
Leaves are a light yellow-green, divided, with broad, toothed lobes. Each
flowerhead looks rather Daisy-like (237), with a yellow centre, surrounded by
short 'petals'. Garden forms with double flowers are not uncommon.
Flowering season: July–Sep
Habitat: Waste ground, walls, old gardens, hedges, roadsides.
Distribution: Native in SE Europe. Introduced and naturalised, as far north as
S Sweden. Throughout BI, but scattered in N and W Scotland, and Ireland.
Uses: Mildly sedative, and reduces inflammation. To relieve migraine and
other headaches, as well as arthritis and asthma. An infusion is taken to
regularise periods, and for tinnitus.

239 Pyrethrum ⊕   *Tanacetum cinerariifolium*
(Daisy Family)
Aromatic perennial with grey-green foliage and slender, ribbed stems,
growing to 45 cm. Leaves finely divided, with silky white hairs beneath.
Flowerheads are large and daisy-like, 3–4 cm across, with yellow centres
and a ring of white ray florets.
Flowering season: July–Sep
Habitat: Rocky, sunny sites.
Distribution: Native in SE Europe. Occasionally cultivated.
Active ingredients: Mainly the natural insecticides cinerin and pyrethrin.
Uses: Dried flowers used as traditional and relatively safe insecticide.

240 Yarrow*   *Achillea millefolium*
(Daisy Family)
Hairy perennial to 60 cm tall, with erect stem, branching towards the top.
Leaves 2–3 pinnate, with narrowly lanceolate tips. Flowerheads 4–8 mm
broad, forming dense umbel-like clusters. Bracts 3–4.5 mm long. Ray
florets white or pinkish. Tube florets yellowish-white. Fruits 1.8–2 mm
long, with somewhat winged margins; without pappus.
Flowering season: June–Oct
Habitat: Grassy sites; meadows, pastures, roadsides, gardens.
Distribution: Europe; N Asia.
Active ingredients: Essential oils, notably cineol and chamazules; bitters; tannins.
Uses: For loss of appetite and digestive problems; also liver and gall-bladder
complaints. In homeopathy to treat internal bleeding. Fresh leaves inhibit
bleeding and are useful on a bandage. Flower-oil used to treat colds and flu.
Further uses: Leaves have sharp, peppery flavour and can be added to
salads. To make a soothing tea, as tonic or to take for colds.
Home use tips: As digestive tonic; also externally to wash wounds. Infuse 2
teaspoonful in 250 ml boiling hot water for 15 minutes. Drink 2–3 cups daily.
Similar species: Sneezewort* ⊕ (*A. ptarmica*) has larger flowerheads, with
a greenish-white central disc. It grows in damp grassy places. Its rhizome is
used for fatigue, flatulence, rheumatism, toothache and urinary disorders.
Note: The generic name comes from the Greek warrior Achilles, who was
said to have used Yarrow to stem bleeding during the Trojan War.

241 Chamomile* ✿

Chamaemelum nobile

(Daisy Family)

Aromatic perennial, to 30 cm tall, with apple-like scent. Leaves alternate and unstalked; deeply and finely dissected. Flowerheads large and daisy-like, with convex centre, 2–2.5 cm across, solitary and stalked, at the ends of stems. Ray florets white; tube florets yellow. Tube florets with swollen bases. Some garden forms have full, double flowers. Receptacle with oblong scales.

Flowering season: June–Oct

Habitat: Dry, sandy grassland; often coastal.

Distribution: W Europe. In BI local, mainly in S Britain and SW Ireland.

Active ingredients: Essential oil with chamazules; bitters; coumarin, flavone-glycosides.

Uses: As appetite stimulant and digestive tonic. A tea from dried flowers relieves nausea and indigestion. On poultice for eczema and wounds.

Further uses: Leaves in pot-pourri. Flower decoction as hair conditioner, and as bath freshener.

242 Scented Mayweed* ✿

Matricaria recutita

(Daisy Family)

Almost hairless annual to 50 cm tall, with upright, branching stems. Leaves alternate, deeply and finely divided. Flowerheads large and daisy-like, with convex centre, 1.8–2.5 cm across, solitary and stalked, at the ends of stems. Ray florets white; tube florets yellow. Receptacle hollow and conical. Whole plant usually has sweet honey-like aroma.

Flowering season: May–Sep

Habitat: Fields, footpaths, waste land; on loamy soils. Sometimes cultivated as a medicinal herb.

Distribution: Most of Europe; W and C Asia. In BI mainly in lowland England and Wales; rare in Scotland. Virtually absent from Ireland.

Active ingredients: Essential oils, notably chamazules; flavonoids; coumarins.

Uses: Anti-inflammatory, used in many preparations and infusions to treat stomach, intestinal and skin problems. Diluted oils aid healing on cuts and soothe eczema. Oil also said to aid liver regeneration.

Home use tips: To treat intestinal inflammation: Infuse 1–2 teaspoonsful in boiling hot water for 10 minutes. Drink 3 cups daily, on an empty stomach. The infusion may also be used externally for skin problems. For bronchial complaints: pour boiling hot water over a small handful of flowers. Inhale the steam for 10 minutes.

Similar species: Scentless Mayweed° (*Tripleurospermum inodorum*) differs in having a solid, not hollow receptacle, and slightly bigger flowers. It also lacks the aroma. In BI a common lowland arable weed.

Ergot* ☠   *Claviceps purpurea*

(Ascomycete fungus)

This is a parasitic fungus that lives on many species of grass, including Rye
and other cereal crops. It produces an overwintering body, the sclerotium,
in the inflorescence (ears) of its host. The sclerotium is 3–50 mm long,
curved and dark brown or violet. Further development takes place the
following spring.

Host species: Mainly Rye, more rarely Barley and Wheat; many wild grasses.
Distribution: Worldwide.
Active ingredients: Alkaloids including those in the lysergic acid group
(LSD can be isolated) and clavines.
Uses: Pure alkaloids used medicinally for treating uterine bleeding. In
homeopathy for circulatory disorders.
NB: Ergot is deadly poisonous. Do not use.
Note: Ergot was the cause of periodic outbreaks of St Anthony's Fire in
medieval times after milling of infected grain.

Field Horsetail*   *Equisetum arvense*

(Horsetail Family)

Vegetative stems to 80 cm tall, 3–5 mm thick, jointed and with 6–20
rounded ridges. Stem sheaths narrowly funnel-shaped, 10–12 mm long,
with 6–20 blackish, triangular, pointed teeth. Branches long, in dense
whorls; simple (rarely branched), hollow and ridged. Cone-bearing stems
appear before the vegetative stems. These are pale brown, about 1–4 cm
tall, with a rounded top.

Spores ripen: Mar–Apr
Habitat: Damp grassy sites, dune-slacks, waste ground, ditches.
Distribution: Europe; Asia; N America.
Active ingredients: Flavone-glycosides, silicic acid, saponins.
Uses: To treat kidney and bladder disorders. Also sometimes used in cases
of bed-wetting, and for arthritis, eczema and ulcers.

Iceland Moss*   *Cetraria islandica*

(Lichen)

Branching lichen, about 4–10 cm tall, growing on the ground. Surfaces flat
and leaf-like, 5–20 mm wide; brown or brownish-green above, pale green
or pale brown below, with bristly margins.
Habitat: Heath, coniferous forest; particularly in the north and in the Alps.
Distribution: Arctic; Antarctic; almost worldwide in mountains.
Active ingredients: Mucilages, various acids, vitamins, iodine.
Uses: To treat chesty coughs, bronchial infections and stomach and
intestinal inflammation. Also used against tuberculosis.
Further uses: Yields a brown dye.

243

244
245

246

Stag's-horn Clubmoss* ☠ *Lycopodium clavatum*

(Clubmoss Family)

Perennial, moss-like, spore-bearing plant, with creeping stem growing up to 4 m long, and occasional vertical branches 5–20 cm tall. Leaves in spirals, linear-lanceolate and pointed, 3–4 mm long, with long, white, hair-like tip. Cones usually paired, 3–6 cm long and 3–4 mm thick, on long stalks.

Spores ripen: June–Aug

Habitat: Heaths, moors, mountains, open woodland, clearings.

Distribution: Europe, except for south; W Asia; N America. In BI throughout, mainly in upland areas.

Active ingredients: The alkaloids lycopodin, clavatin and clavotoxin.

Uses: In homeopathy for liver, gall-bladder and digestive problems, kidney and bladder complaints, rheumatism and gout.

NB: Poisonous. Do not collect, or prepare at home.

Maidenhair Fern* ✿ *Adiantum capillus-veneris*

(Maidenhair Fern Family)

Delicate fern with creeping rhizome, arched fronds with fan-shaped leaflets and thin, shiny black stalks, with thin brown scales at base. Leaves pale green with toothed leaflets.

Spores ripen: June–Sep

Habitat: Damp sites, around springs, cave entrances, limestone pavement and cliffs; also occasionally on walls and buildings.

Distribution: Many warm regions including the Mediterranean area. In BI scattered, mainly in western parts.

Active ingredients: Tannins, bitters, sugar, essential oil.

Uses: As expectorant for coughs and bronchial catarrh.

247

248

Male Fern* ⊛ ☠☘

Dryopteris filix-mas

(Buckler-fern Family)

Large fern with short rhizome covered with brown, scaly leaf remnants.
Leaves pale green, to 1.3 m tall, often growing out in a funnel-shaped
clump. Blade 2–3 times longer than stalk. Stalk thick, pale brown and
covered with brown scales. Blade long, narrowing towards the tip, pinnate,
with deeply divided lobes. About 20–35 first-order lobes on each side of
blade. Sporangia (lower left) in 2 rows, on underside of upper part of leaf.
Spores ripen: July–Sep
Habitat: Woods, banks, ditches, mountains.
Distribution: Europe; N Asia; N America. In BI common throughout.
Active ingredients: Phloroglucine derivatives, tannins, bitters.
Uses: Previously as treatment for tapeworm. No longer used because of its
toxic side-effects.
NB: Poisonous. Do not collect or use.

Polypody*

Polypodium vulgare

(Polypody Family)

Medium-sized fern with long, scaly rhizome. Leaves to 60 cm long, growing
erect, in 2 rows along rhizome. Leaf stalk yellow or greenish, usually
shorter than blade. Latter leathery, linear to narrowly lanceolate, of even
width over much of its length, then narrowing rather abruptly towards the
tip. About 7–28 rather blunt lobes on each side. Sporangia rounded, in
2 rows, on either side of lobe's midrib.
Spores ripen: July–Aug
Habitat: Open woodland, shady rocks, banks, old trees, walls. Often
epiphytic in damp areas.
Distribution: Europe, except for south; N Asia; N America. In BI common
throughout.
Active ingredients: Tannins, saponins, essential oil, mucilages, sugar.
Uses: In medicine (rarely) for coughs, hoarseness, gall-bladder complaints
and as a mild laxative.

Norway Spruce* ⚘

Picea abies

(Pine Family)

Evergreen, coniferous tree growing to 50 m tall, with a pointed, conical
crown and branches growing in whorls. Trunk to 2 m across, straight. Bark
at first smooth and pale brown, later red-brown to grey and flaky. Branches
regular and more or less horizontal, giving layered appearance. New growth
with pointed buds, without resinous covering. Needles almost rectangular,
sharply pointed, 25–35 mm long, inserted spirally and growing from small
brown pegs – stalk-like extensions of the stem. Male flowers found over the
entire crown of tree, 1.5–3 cm long, cylindrical, at first red, becoming
yellow. Female flowers only at the very top of the tree; at first red, erect,
6 cm long, later drooping cones, 10–15 cm long, brown, with oval scales.
Seeds 4–5 mm long, with a 15 mm pale brown, translucent wing.

Flowering season: May–June

Habitat: Forms woods in Europe in cool, damp mountain sites
above 800 m (montane and sub-alpine zone), in the Alps to about 2000 m.
Also very widely planted outside this region as a forestry tree.

Distribution: Much of Europe and W Asia. In BI introduced and much planted.

Active ingredients: Essential oil.

Uses: Oil used medicinally in embrocation to treat muscular pain and
rheumatism. Extract of needles as a bath tonic.

Further uses: To make a type of beer. As a Christmas Tree.

Silver Fir* ⚘

Abies alba

(Pine Family)

Evergreen, coniferous tree growing to 50 m tall and 2 m across, with crown
at first conical and pointed, later columnar with rather flattened top. Trunk
straight with silver-grey, smooth bark, and almost horizontal branches. New
growth roughly hairy; buds oval, without resinous covering. Needles to
25 mm long and 3 mm wide, with 2 whitish waxy stripes below, and
spreading on upper side of twig to reveal parting. Male flowers 2–3 cm
long, cylindrical, yellowish, clumped beneath shoot. Female flowers pale
green, in upright cones, about 6 cm long and pale green at first, 8–16 cm
long when ripe, remaining erect and falling off to leave just the central axis
behind (typical of firs). Cones have prominent bracts between the scales.
Seeds 8–12 mm long, winged.

Flowering season: May–June

Habitat: Middle and upper tree zones (in Alps to 1600 m); often with
Beech and Norway Spruce. On all soils, preferring sites with high air
humidity and soil moisture.

Distribution: Mountains of C and S Europe. Widely planted.

Active ingredients: Essential oils, including pinene, limonene and others.

Uses: Essential oil in various preparations for rheumatism circulatory
problems, and as inhalant for bronchial problems. Essence also used in
cough sweets and to give 'pine' scent to toiletries.

Further uses: The original Christmas Tree.

Note: The related N American Balsam Fir (*A. balsamea*) yields Canada
Balsam from its resin. This is used in gargles and inhalants.

Scots Pine* ☙

Pinus sylvestris

(Pine Family)

Evergreen conifer growing to 40 m tall. Crown at first conical with
branches in whorls, later spreading and irregular. Bark reddish-brown and
flaky towards top of the trunk; grey or brown, roughly furrowed and
cracking lower down. Needles paired on short shoots, 3–7 cm long, stiff,
pointed, blue-green, with semi-circular cross-section. Male flowers
clustered at the base of young shoots, cylindrical, 5–8 mm long and yellow.
Female cones erect, solitary or in pairs (rarely in fours), terminal, about
5 mm long and dark red or violet at first; ripening to oval, 3–7 cm long,
grey-brown. Scales usually without an obvious spine. Seeds ripen in the
autumn of the second year and are shed in the following spring, after which
the cones fall off the tree entire.

Flowering season: May

Habitat: Mainly in lowlands, but in mountains to over 2000 m. In Europe
its natural habitat is in the more extreme sites (for example those on very
dry, poor sandy, sometimes boggy soils). Widely planted throughout.

Distribution: C and N Europe; Turkey; N Asia. In BI, native to Scotland;
widely planted.

Active ingredients: Essential oils including phellandrene and pinene,
tannin, bitters.

Uses: Essential oil used as constituent of inhalants for respiratory ailments,
and in embrocation for rheumatism and to stimulate circulation.

Further uses: To make a refreshing tea. Distilled pine oil used in perfumes
and soaps.

Home use tips: Add a handful of shoot tips to the bath to ease rheumatic
pains and to improve the circulation.

Mountain Pine/Dwarf Mountain Pine ☙

(Pine Family)

Pinus mugo

Evergreen coniferous shrub, growing to 6 m tall. Bark brown-black, scaly.
Buds with shiny covering of resin. Needles paired, 1–5 cm long and 1.5 mm
wide, with semi-circular cross-section. Male flowers clustered in spirals,
yellow. Female cones 5 mm long at first, red, round or oval, at tips of new
growth, erect; 2–5 cm long and 1.5–2.5 cm wide when ripe.

Flowering season: June–July

Habitat: In pure stands at the tree-line in mountains.

Distribution: Alps and other ranges of C and E Europe.

Active ingredients: Essential oils including phellandrene, pinene and
limonene.

Uses: Essential oil used as constituent of inhalants for respiratory ailments,
and in embrocation and bath oils for rheumatism and to stimulate
circulation.

254

255

256 Italian Cypress ✤   *Cupressus sempervirens*
(Cypress Family)

Evergreen conifer to about 30 m tall. Commonest planted form densely branched. Stems rounded or weakly rectangular (never flat). Leaves scale-like. Male flowers club-shaped, 3–6 mm long, first yellow-green, later brownish. Female flowers about 4–6 mm, in rounded cones, green, clustered near shoot-tips. Ripe cones rounded, grey-brown, shiny, 2.5–4 cm across, with 6–12 protective scales each with central pointed projection.

Flowering season: Apr

Habitat: Natural habitat is montane forest, especially rocky, open and sunny sites. Tolerates summer droughts, and requires mild winters.

Distribution: E Mediterranean, SW Asia. Now throughout Mediterranean.

Active ingredients: Essential oil.

Uses: Oil used as constituent of inhalants and in embrocations for coughs, whooping cough and asthma. Also used to treat broken capillaries and heavy periods, varicose veins and haemorrhoids.

Further uses: As constituent of perfumes, aftershaves and soaps.

257 Common Juniper❋ ✤   *Juniperus communis*
(Cypress Family)

Evergreen shrub or small tree growing to 12 m tall, with shaggy growth. Very variable in shape. Needles in whorls of 3; to 2 cm long and 2 mm wide, stiff and sharply pointed. Male and female flowers on separate plants, in the axils of young needles. Male flowers oval, 4–5 mm long, yellow. Female flowers 2 mm across, growing in small green cones. Cones berry-like, 4–9 mm across; first green, ripening (in the 2nd or 3rd year) to blue-black.

Flowering season: May–June

Habitat: From the lowland to the mountains (Alps to 1900 m). Open pinewoods, sunny rocky sites, heaths and poor grassland.

Distribution: Europe, N Asia, N America.

Active ingredients: Essential oil, tannins, resin.

Uses: Essential oil used in various preparations as an embrocation for rheumatism, and as an inhalant for bronchitis.

Further uses: Berries in gin and jenever, herbal tea. Also used as a spice.

Home use tips: A tea to treat diarrhoea and flatulence. Use equal amounts of Juniper berries and Lovage root. Infuse 2 teaspoonsful in 250 ml boiling water for 10 minutes. Drink 1–2 cups daily.

258 Savin ⚕☒   *Juniperus sabina*
(Cypress Family)

Evergreen shrub or small coniferous tree growing to 4 m tall. Leaves opposite, scale-like, 1–2.5 mm long, strongly aromatic, grey-green or blue-green. Cones berry-like, dark blue, with white bloom, 3–7 mm across.

Flowering season: Mar–May.

Habitat: Rocky slopes, scrub.

Distribution: Mountains of S and C Europe; C Asia; NW China.

Active ingredients: Yields oil of savarin.

Uses: In homeopathy for menstrual problems. Young twigs are insecticidal.

NB: Poisonous. Do not prepare at home.

256

257

258

Ginkgo/Maidenhair Tree ✿   *Ginkgo biloba*

(Ginkgo Family)

Deciduous tree growing to 30 m tall, with an irregular, much-branched crown, narrow in young trees, broadening with age. Trunk straight and becoming rather wide. Leaves solitary and alternate on long shoots, arranged in small whorls (usually of 3) on newer shoots. Leaves fan-shaped, 5–8 cm across, long-stalked and with a leathery texture, with sub-parallel veins, radiating out from base of leaf; pale green at first, turning dark green and yellow in the autumn. Outer edge of leaf undulating or notched, often with a deep central notch dividing leaf into two lobes. Dioecious. Male flowers in catkin-like clusters of 2–5, 4–7 cm long, yellow, with many stamens. Female flowers long-stalked in groups of 1–3, green. Seed fleshy, plum-like, yellow-green, ripening to yellow-orange, with an unpleasant smell, rather like rancid butter.

Flowering season: Apr–May

Habitat: In native range, mixed woods at about 750 m. Widely planted.

Distribution: SE China. Common park and garden tree in Europe. In BI, mainly in S England.

Active ingredients: Flavonoids, ginkgetine.

Uses: Medicinally in preparations to treat circulatory problems, particularly in older people. Leaves and seeds used in Chinese medicine for lung problems.

Note: Recent research has shown that an extract strengthens blood vessels and reduces the production of free radicals (which damage tissues).

Joint-pine   *Ephedra distachya*

(Joint-pine Family)

Low-growing trailing shrub, growing to 50 cm tall, with underground rhizome. Stems green and finely striped; rather stiff, straight or arching. Leaves very small and scale-like, to 2 mm long, green with white papery margins, opposite, fused and sheathing stem towards base. Dioecious. Male inflorescence sessile or stalked, with 4–8 pairs of flowers, each with a single stamen filament bearing several anthers. Female inflorescence of 2 flowers and usually 3 pairs of bracts. Inflorescence 6–7 mm in diameter, fleshy, red and berry-like when ripe.

Flowering season: Mar–May

Habitat: Warm, dry, rocky, sites; often coastal.

Distribution: S Europe; Asia.

Active ingredients: The alkaloids ephedrine and pseudoephedrine, tannin, saponin.

Uses: Ephedrine narrows blood vessels and is useful for stabilising blood pressure, and as a nasal decongestant. Nowadays mostly prepared synthetically.

Note: The related *E. sinica* has been used in traditional Chinese medicine for 5,000 years.

Common Couch*

(Grass Family)   *Elytrigia (Elymus/Agropyron) repens*

Perennial grass to 1.5 m tall, with long, pale, creeping and branching rhizomes. Stem erect, hairless. Leaves linear and sheathing, with long, pointed overlapping auricles at base. Leaf blade 3–10 mm wide, with scattered long hairs on upper surface. Spikelets (each with 3–8 florets) in 2 rows on spike axis, sessile; glumes 7–12 mm; lemmas 8–12 mm.

Flowering season: June–July

Habitat: Fields, gardens, waysides.

Distribution: Europe; N Asia; N Africa; N America.

Active ingredients: Carbohydrates, mucilages, silicic acid, saponins.

Uses: As diuretic to treat urinary problems.

Home use tips: As diuretic and purifier. Boil 2 teaspoonsful of rhizome in 250 ml water. Drink 2 cups daily.

Oats* ✿

(Grass Family)   *Avena sativa*

Annual grass to 1.5 m tall. Stem branching from base. Leaf sheaths hairless, with short ligule; no auricles. Blade narrow, rough on both sides. Spikelets in broad panicle. Glumes longer than lemmas.

Flowering season: June–Aug

Habitat: Cultivated. Rough ground, waysides.

Distribution: W Mediterranean. In BI as crop and casual.

Active ingredients: Starch, protein, fat, saponin, minerals, vitamin E.

Uses: In homeopathy to treat insomnia and nervous fatigue. Oat bran helps reduce cholesterol. A decoction treats colds, depression, menopausal problems, muscular sclerosis and shingles.

Further uses: Fine oatmeal as soothing wash for dry skin. Rolled oats used to make porridge.

Two-rowed Barley* ✿

(Grass Family)   *Hordeum distichon*

Annual almost hairless grass growing to 75 cm. Leaves with 2 stem-encircling auricles at top of sheath. Spikelets in terminal spike, arranged in 2 rows. Lemmas with long awns.

Flowering season: May–June

Habitat: Cultivated. Rough ground, waysides.

Distribution: SW Asia. Cultivated and casual.

Active ingredients: Carbohydrates, proteins, minerals, vitamins.

Uses: Medicinally to stimulate the circulation. Cooked barley on a poultice to soothe sores.

Further uses: For cereals and meal, and, as pearl barley, for soups and stews. To produce beer and whisky, using malted grain.

Note: This is the most commonly cultivated barley. Six-rowed and four-rowed forms also occur; these are classified as *H. vulgare*.

Sand Sedge*

Carex arenaria

(Sedge Family)

Grass-like, with extensive rhizome. Stems triangular, to 40 cm tall. Leaves 3–4 mm wide, stiff. Inflorescence of 6–16 almost sessile spikelets; lower ones female, upper ones with both male and female flowers. Bracts brownish, narrowly oval, pointed. Nut enclosed in a beaked false fruit formed by the extra inner glume (the utricle).

Flowering season: May–June

Habitat: Sandy heaths, dunes; mainly coastal.

Distribution: Most of Europe.

Active ingredients: Saponins, tannins, silicic acid, glycosides, mucilage, starch, some essential oil.

Uses: Medicinally as diuretic and to induce sweating.

Sweet-flag*

Acorus calamus

(Arum Family)

Hairless perennial to 1.5 m tall, with stiff, grass-like leaves about 2 cm wide, and triangular stem. Leaves have spicy aroma when crushed. Inflorescence a cylindrical greenish-yellow spadix pointing out to one side and up to about 9 cm long. Flowers all very small and hermaphrodite, with yellowish-green perianth segments less than 1 mm long. Fruit (not often developed) a reddish berry.

Flowering season: May–July

Habitat: In still or slow-flowing water with a muddy bottom. Reedbeds and sedge communities.

Distribution: Much of Europe; Asia; N America. In BI introduced; locally naturalised, mainly in lowland England.

Active ingredients: Essential oil with asarone, bitters, tannins.

Uses: To treat loss of appetite, and stomach, intestine and gallbladder problems. Used in Chinese medicine for arthritis, epilepsy and strokes.

Further uses: The leaves and rhizomes repel insects.

Home use tips: For loss of appetite and nervous stomach. Infuse 2 teaspoonsful of root in 250 ml boiling water for 15 minutes. Drink 1 cup, lukewarm, twice daily.

Herb Paris* ☠

Paris quadrifolia

(Lily Family)

Hairless perennial to 40 cm tall with an erect stem, often growing in colonies. Leaves in a whorl at tip of stem, usually 4, sometimes 5 or 6. Leaf surface has a noticeable network of veins. Flowers terminal, on a 2–5 cm stalk. Perianth segments green, in 2 whorls of 4, lanceolate to linear. Stamens 8 (rarely more). Fruit a black, round berry to 1 cm across, opening when ripe.

Flowering season: May–June

Habitat: Deciduous (rarely coniferous) woods; prefers moist calcareous soil.

Distribution: Most of Europe; Asia. In Britain rather local, mainly in the east. Absent from Ireland.

Active ingredients: Saponins, organic acids.

Uses: In homeopathy to treat nervous pains of head and face, also laryngitis.

NB: Poisonous. Do not prepare at home.

269 Purple Willow* ✿ ⚘

Salix purpurea

(Willow Family)

Shrub or small tree growing to 10 m tall. Twigs thin, cane–like, stiffly upright.
Leaves alternate (can be opposite) lanceolate and pointed, wider in lower
third, 4–12 cm long and up to 1.5 cm wide, finely toothed towards tip, hairless
on both sides, dark green above and blue-green below. Male catkins erect, to 5
cm long, each with 2 fused stamens; anthers at first purple-red, turning yellow.
Female catkins to 2 cm long; ovary with white silky hairs.

Flowering season: Mar–May

Habitat: River valley woods, ditches, other damp soils. Also a pioneer
species of sandy, muddy or gravelly flooded sites.

Distribution: Europe; Asia; N Africa. In BI scattered, often planted.

Active ingredients: Salicylates, glycosides, tannins.

Uses: To reduce fevers and inflammation, for rheumatism and gastroenteritis.

270 Aspen*

Populus tremula

(Willow Family)

Deciduous tree, to 24 m tall, with broad, open crown and grey-green bark
becoming darker and ridged with age. Leaves with long, laterally flattened
stalks. Blade 3–8(15) cm across, rounded to oval, hairy only when young; shiny
green above, paler beneath. Male flowers in dense, dangling catkins to 11 cm
long, at first reddish, then paler, each with 4–12 stamens. Female flowers in
reddish catkins of similar length; ovary green, with 2 purple stigmas. Fruit a
2-valved capsule releasing small seeds with cottony hairs in May–June.

Flowering season: Mar–Apr

Habitat: Open woodland, clearings and woodland edges.

Distribution: Europe; N Asia; N Africa.

Active ingredients: Various salicylates, flavone-glycosides, tannins.

Uses: In homeopathy to treat cystitis, prostate trouble and arthritis.

271 Walnut* ✿

Juglans regia

(Walnut Family)

Deciduous tree growing to 25 m tall, with a broad trunk, loose, open crown,
heavy branches and deeply fissured, dark grey bark. Leaves alternate,
long-stalked, pinnate, 20–45 cm long with 5–9 (usually 7) elliptical leaflets;
aromatic when crushed. Male flowers in drooping catkins to 15 cm long.
Female flowers in stiff clusters of 1–5. Fruit a single-seeded round to oval
drupe, 4–5 cm across. The outer husk is shiny and green at first, ripening to
brown. This encloses a hard, woody nut containing the familiar edible walnut.

Flowering season: Apr–May

Habitat: Mainly planted. Naturalised in mixed river-valley woodland.

Distribution: Originally SE Europe, SW and C Asia. Cultivated in S and C
Europe and occasionally naturalised. In BI planted, especially in S and SW.

Active ingredients: Tannins, essential oil, juglone, flavonoids.

Uses: To treat stomach and intestinal inflammation, also skin problems.

Further uses: Nuts eaten fresh, in salads, or pickled. Walnut oil used in
salad dressing, and in soaps. Leaves and husks yield a brown dye.

Home use tips: For stomach problems and eczema. Put 2 teaspoonsful in
250 ml cold water; boil for 3–5 minutes. Drink 2–3 cups daily or use as a wash.

269

270

271

272 Silver Birch* ✿ ❀

Betula pendula

(Birch Family)

Deciduous tree to 30 m tall, with branches sharply angled upwards, tending to curve downwards towards the tips. Bark shiny, reddish-brown at first, later pinkish or white with pale grey horizontal markings; knobbly and fissured towards base. Young shoots shiny, red-brown, with many wart-like glands. Leaves alternate; stalk 2–3 cm long, hairless; blade triangular, tapering to a point, 4–7 cm long, doubly toothed. Male and female flowers separate on same tree. Male catkins yellow-brown and drooping, narrowly cylindrical, to 10 cm long. Female flowers in stalked, slender green catkins, 2–3 cm long.

Flowering season: Apr–May

Habitat: Forms woods on light, acid soils. Also woodland edges, fens and bogs, heaths, wasteland. Widely planted in parks and along roads.

Distribution: Europe; N Asia. In BI commoner towards the south.

Active ingredients: Flavone-glycosides, tannins, essential oil.

Uses: Leaves are anti-bacterial. Medicinally to treat fluid retention, kidney and bladder complaints, rheumatism and gout. Also reduces cholesterol.

Further uses: Oils used in some soaps. Syrup and wine can be made from the sap. Leaves yield green and yellow dyes.

Home use tips: To treat fluid retention. Infuse 2 teaspoonsful in boiling water for 10 minutes. Drink 3 cups daily.

273 274 Pedunculate Oak* ✿ ❀

Quercus robur

(Beech Family)

Deciduous tree growing to 50 m tall, with irregular and spreading crown, and trunk usually branching fairly low down. Bark grey-green and shiny at first, becoming thick, grey-brown, and ridged. Leaves alternate, with 2–7 mm long stalk; blade obovate to wedge-shaped, hairless, 5–15 cm long, with 3–6 lobes at each side. Leaf-base heart-shaped, with auricles. Male flowers in drooping yellow-green catkins, 2–4 cm long. Female flowers in stalked spikes of 1–6 flowers, usually with reddish, 3-lobed stigma. Fruits the familiar acorns, borne on long stalks (2–10 cm) in groups of 3(5). Each acorn 2–3 cm long, in scaly cup; green at first, ripening to brown, sometimes with dark longitudinal stripes.

Flowering season: Apr–May

Habitat: Mixed broad-leaved woodland, from lowland to montane levels. Long planted in woodland, parks and along streets.

Distribution: Europe. In BI throughout, but less frequent in N and W.

Active ingredients: Tannins (to 20%).

Uses: The bark is antiseptic and reduces bleeding. Decoction applied to cuts and burns, and to treat skin infections and frost-bite; gargle for sore throats.

Further uses: The very young leaves make a good, dry wine. Acorns fed to pigs.

Home use tips: For use on poultice for skin complaints. Boil 1–2 teaspoonsful in water for 3–5 minutes.

Similar species: Sessile Oak* ❀ (*Q. petraea*) has leaf stalks 1–3 cm long, almost sessile acorns, and auricles absent or only weakly developed. W, C and S Europe. In BI throughout, particularly in N and W.

Note: Trees (presumed hybrids) with intermediate characters often occur where Sessile Oak and English Oak are both found. Such hybrid trees are common in the British Isles.

Sweet Chestnut* ⊛

Castanea sativa

(Beech Family)

Broad-crowned deciduous tree to about 30 m tall. Bark smooth and olive-brown at first, becoming grey-brown with vertical spiral ridges. Young shoots smooth and olive-green or olive-brown. Leaves alternate, leathery. Stalk 1–2.5 cm long, blade narrowly elliptical to lanceolate, pointed, 8–25 cm long, edged with coarse, bristly teeth; shiny dark green above, paler below with felty hairs when young, becoming hairless later. Flowers in long, stiff catkins, 10–20 cm long; mostly male, but female towards the base. Female flowers either solitary or in groups of 2 or 3, at the base of the male catkins and surrounded by a green, scaly husk. Fruit a shiny dark brown, leathery, edible nut (the familiar chestnut) about 2–3 cm long. Up to 3 nuts enclosed in brownish-yellow spiny husk, opening into 4 sections when ripe.

Flowering season: June

Habitat: Sub-Mediterranean mixed oak woodland in regions with mild winters, warm summers, and relatively high rainfall; usually on acid soils.

Distribution: S Europe; Turkey; Caucasus; N Africa. Naturalised locally in C and S Europe. In BI planted throughout, especially in SE England, where sometimes naturalised.

Active ingredients: Tannins, flavonoids, starch (nuts).

Uses: In various preparations for coughs.

Further uses: Chestnuts have a long history of use as food, either the nuts themselves, or ground into flour. Yields rot-proof timber for fence posts and the like. Used in some shampoos.

Asarabacca* ⚕☠☒

Asarum europaeum

(Birthwort Family)

Perennial to 10 cm tall with a creeping stem covered with soft, pale hairs. Leaves in pairs (sometimes 3 or 4), dark green and kidney-shaped with a shiny, leathery surface. Flowers solitary and terminal, short-stalked and with peppery smell. Perianth bell-shaped, 3-lobed, fused at the base, 1–1.5 cm long, greenish on the outside and reddish-brown inside. Stamens 12, in two rows, the outer ones shorter than the inner. Ovary inferior, with a short, broad style and 6-lobed stigma. Fruit a leathery, rounded, 6-celled capsule.

Flowering season: Apr–May

Habitat: Mixed deciduous woods, mostly on calcareous soils.

Distribution: Most of Europe; N Asia. In Britain doubtfully native. Rather a rare and decreasing species. Absent from Ireland.

Active ingredients: Essential oil, notably asarone; tannins; flavonoids.

Uses: In homeopathy to treat nausea, nervous exhaustion, and to improve blood circulation to the hands. Also said to be an anti-asthmatic and immune stimulant.

NB: Poisonous. Do not prepare at home.

275

276

277

Small-leaved Elm* ⊛   *Ulmus minor*

(Elm Family)

Very variable deciduous tree growing to 30 m tall. Leaves alternate;
variable in size and shape. Usually short-stalked, with elliptic narrowly
pointed blade, with an asymmetrical base. Margin once or twice-toothed.
Usually hairless above and shiny dark green; hairs restricted to vein axils
beneath. Flowers each about 3 mm long, in clusters, opening before the
leaves. Fruit (top photo) a 2-winged achene, 13–25 mm long.

Flowering season: Mar–Apr

Habitat: Mixed deciduous woodland, hedgerows. Often planted in parks
and along roads.

Distribution: Europe (excluding Scandinavia). In BI mainly in S and
C England.

Active ingredients: Mucilage, tannins, flavonoids.

Uses: In homeopathy to treat pains in hand and foot joints. Also a
constituent of ointment for haemorrhoids.

Stinging Nettle*   *Urtica dioica*

(Nettle Family)

Perennial to 1.5 m tall, covered with stinging hairs. Leaves opposite, stalked,
heart-shaped at the base, pointed and broadly toothed. Flowers clustered in
the leaf axils. Plant dioecious. Perianth segments 4, small and greenish.

Flowering season: July–Oct

Habitat: Waste ground, clearings, woods, fens, garden weed.

Distribution: Worldwide, in temperate regions.

Active ingredients: Iron, ammonia, formic acid, silicic acid, histamine,
acetylcholine.

Uses: Relieves symptoms of rheumatism and sciatica. Also lowers blood
pressure and improves the circulation; also as a diuretic. As iron-rich tea for
anaemia. On a poultice to treat eczema.

Further uses: As a vegetable (fresh shoots and leaves), and to make beer.

Home use tips: For rheumatism and urinary problems. Boil 2 teaspoonsful
in 250 ml water for 5 minutes. Drink 1 cup each morning and evening.

Note: Several butterfly species feed on nettles as larvae. A stingless form
grows in some fenland habitats; this has obvious potential as a garden or
cultivated plant.

Small Nettle*   *Urtica urens*

(Nettle Family)

Annual to 60 cm tall, covered with stinging hairs. Leaves 1–5 cm long,
long-stalked, elliptic or oval, wedge-shaped at the base, pointed and
toothed. Flowers clustered in the leaf axils. Plant monoecious, but female
flowers more numerous.

Flowering season: May–Nov

Habitat: Cultivated and waste ground, garden weed.

Distribution: Europe; Asia; N America. In BI commonest in the east.

Active ingredients: See Stinging Nettle.

Uses: In homeopathy to treat nettle-rash (urticaria), light burns and arthritis.

Home use tips: See Stinging Nettle.

Fig* ✤   *Ficus carica*

(Mulberry Family)

A short-trunked deciduous shrub or tree with a rounded, open crown growing to about 10 m. Bark brown or grey, smooth. Leaves alternate, with 4–8 cm long stalk. Blade thick and leathery, dark green above and roughly hairy, 8–20 cm long and similar width; mostly deeply palmately lobed, with 3–5(7) lobes; heart-shaped at base. The wild form is monoecious; cultivated forms are dioecious. Individual flowers small, growing inside pear-shaped fleshy receptacle. Female flowers in the base, male flowers towards the narrow opening at top. The familiar fig is a pear-shaped fleshy fruit, 5–8 cm long, green, brown or brownish-violet. The tasty ripe flesh contains the tiny seeds.

Flowering season: June–Sep

Habitat: Dry rocky slopes, maquis, alongside stone walls and rivers.

Distribution: Mediterranean region, north to S Alps; Turkey; W Asia. Widely cultivated in areas with a similar climate throughout the world. In BI, introduced and naturalised in some areas, mainly in the south.

Active ingredients: Invert-sugar, pectin, vitamins, fruit acids, enzymes, mucilage.

Uses: Mild laxative.

Further uses: Eaten as fruit. The leaves yield a yellow dye.

Note: There are two types of cultivated Fig. Trees with fertile female flowers, which produce edible figs, and trees with both male and female flowers, which are mainly cultivated to ensure the supply of the Fig Gallwasp (*Blastophaga psenes*). This type of fig can develop ripe fruit only when grown close to the fertile forms. Most more recent cultivars, however, are able to develop fruit without pollination. Wild Figs, on the other hand, carry three different stages of inflorescence on the same tree. The summer generation develops into ripe figs, the spring generation produces pollen, and ensures, as does the autumn generation, the successful reproduction of the Fig Gallwasp.

Hop* ✤   *Humulus lupulus*

(Hemp Family)

A roughly-hairy climbing perennial growing to about 6 m. Leaves stalked, opposite, mostly 3–7 lobed, with heart-shaped base. Plant dioecious. Male flowers (photo below left), each about 3 mm long, in a loose, many-flowered panicle. Perianth segments 5, greenish; stamens 5. Female flowers in pale green cone-like, stalked clusters, with oval, glandular bracts up to 2 cm long.

Flowering season: July–Sep

Habitat: River woodland and scrub; hedgerows.

Distribution: Most of Europe; N Asia; N America. Widely cultivated for flavouring beer. In BI, grown mainly in SE and C England; widely naturalised.

Active ingredients: Glands produce sap rich in humulon and lupulon; essential oil; tannins.

Uses: Mild sedative. In homeopathy as sedative and to treat nervous stomach problems.

Further uses: Traditional ingredient of beer, to which it gives a bitter flavour. Young shoots make a tasty vegetable; very good in an omelette. Essential oil used in some lotions and perfumes.

Home use tips: For nervous insomnia. Infuse 2 teaspoonsful in 250 ml boiling water for 15 minutes. Drink 2 cups daily.

281

284　Mistletoe*

Viscum album

(Mistletoe Family)

Semi-parasitic evergreen shrub growing as more or less circular clumps to 2 m across, in the branches of trees. Stem greenish-brown, regularly forking, with inconspicuous yellowish flowers. Leaves opposite, leathery, yellowish-green, narrowly obovate. Plant dioecious. Male flowers with 4-partite perianth and 4 stamens. Female flowers with inferior ovary. Fruit a pea-sized white, 1-seeded berry.

Flowering season: Mar–Apr

Habitat: On various trees, notably apples and poplars.

Distribution: Europe; Asia; N Africa. In Britain, mainly in S Welsh borders, and S and E England. Absent from Ireland and most of Scotland.

Active ingredients: Viscotoxin, choline, histamine.

Uses: To treat high blood pressure, arthritis, and to support cancer therapy.

Note: Sacred to the Druids. The habit of kissing underneath it at Christmas relates to its ancient use as a fertility symbol.

285　Common Sorrel*

Rumex acetosa

(Dock Family)

Hairless perennial to 1 m tall, with simple, erect stems. Basal leaves long and arrow-shaped, long-stalked, with acute basal lobes, 4 times as long as wide. Stem leaves rather shorter, the uppermost sessile and clasping the stem. Inflorescence narrow, reddish-green. Plant dioecious. Perianth segments 6, the outer ones smaller and turned back, the inner ones (in female flowers) rounded, 3–3.5 mm long, enclosing the achene.

Flowering season: May–July

Habitat: Meadows, pasture, weedy grassland.

Distribution: Europe; N Asia; N America.

Active ingredients: Potassium oxalate, oxalic acid, flavone-glycosides, vitamin C.

Uses: Leaf tea as diuretic for some kidney and liver complaints, and to reduce fevers. Leaf poultice to treat acne, boils and wounds. Root is mild laxative.

Further uses: Leaves used in salads, as garnish, in soups and as a sauce. The juice bleaches stains.

Home use tips: As tonic tea. Infuse 2 teaspoonsful in 250 ml boiling water for 10 minutes. Drink 2 cups daily.

286　Monk's-rhubarb*

Rumex pseudoalpinus

(Dock Family)

Rhizomatous perennial to 2 m tall. Basal leaves to 50 cm long, broad heart-shaped, long-stalked, with wavy margin. Stem leaves narrower. Inflorescence dense, erect, greenish-yellow. Perianth segments 6, outer ones smaller, inner ones broadly oval, with heart-shaped base, 4–6 mm long, enclosing achene.

Flowering season: June–Aug

Habitat: Meadows, mountain pasture; on nitrogen-rich soils. By roads, streams and old buildings.

Distribution: C and S Europe. Introduced to BI; scattered, mainly in Scotland and N England (relic of ancient cultivation). Absent from Ireland.

Active ingredients: Anthraquinones, essential oil, tannin.

Uses: In homeopathy to treat coughs, bronchitis and diarrhoea.

287 Spear-leaved Orache* *Atriplex prostrata*

(Goosefoot Family)

Trailing or erect annual, often mealy when young. Lower leaves triangular
or spear-shaped, usually toothed. Upper leaves lanceolate. Flowers small,
in panicles. Male flowers 5-partite and with 5 stamens. Female flowers lacking
perianth, but surrounded by a pair of triangular bracts.

Flowering season: June–Sep
Habitat: Waste and cultivated ground; often coastal.
Distribution: Most of Europe; Asia; N America.
Active ingredients: Saponins, minerals.
Uses: Formerly used medicinally to treat bladder, lung and liver ailments,
and to purify the blood.

288 Garden Orache* ✿ *Atriplex hortensis*

(Goosefoot Family)

Erect annual to 2.5 m tall, often mealy when young. Stem striped white and
green. Leaves short-stalked, green or purplish-red, often over 10 cm long,
triangular, entire or toothed. Inflorescence a dense, terminal panicle. Male
flowers small, with 5 stamens. Female flowers lacking perianth, but
surrounded by a pair of rounded or heart-shaped bracts, 1.5 cm long.

Flowering season: July–Aug
Habitat: Waste ground.
Distribution: Origin unknown; possibly Asia. In BI, introduced and
sometimes grown; also from bird-seed.
Active ingredients: Saponins, minerals.
Uses: To treat sore throats, gout and jaundice. Root, stem or flower poultice
to treat insect bites.
Further uses: Leaves and young shoots in salads, or cooked like spinach.
Home use tips: To purify blood and skin. Infuse 1 teaspoonful in 250 ml
boiling water for 10 minutes. Drink 1–2 cups daily.

289 Smooth Rupturewort* ☒ *Herniaria glabra*

(Pink Family)

Prostrate, creeping annual or perennial, with much-branched, rather brittle
stem. Leaves 3–8 mm long, opposite and oval, with fleshy stipules. Flowers
small, rounded, and unstalked, in the leaf axils. Sepals 5, greenish, about
0.5 mm long. Petals tiny.

Flowering season: July–Sep
Habitat: Sandy sites, footpaths, gravel.
Distribution: Europe; W Asia. In BI, a rarity of E England (notably in
Breckland).
Active ingredients: Saponins, flavonoids, coumarins, tannin, essential oil.
Uses: Medicinally to treat chronic cystitis and renal colic.
NB: Rare species. Do not collect.

Black Currant* ❀

Ribes nigrum

(Gooseberry Family)

Deciduous, thornless shrub, to 2 m tall, with musky smell when crushed.
Leaves large, stalked, rounded, 3–5 lobed, with heart-shaped base, smooth
above, hairy and with yellowish glands beneath. Lobes triangular or oval,
pointed, double-toothed. Flowers stalked, in drooping racemes. Calyx
bell-shaped, 5-lobed, hairy. Petals 5, whitish-green, small and erect. Fruit a
round, black berry, 10–15 mm across.

Flowering season: Apr–May

Habitat: Woods, hedges, streamsides.

Distribution: C and N Europe; N Asia. In BI, throughout; probably
introduced.

Active ingredients: Tannin, rutin, vitamin C, essential oil.

Uses: Leaf tea for colds, diarrhoea and sore throats. Also used to treat
dropsy, urine retention and rheumatism.

Further uses: Fruit used in jams, desserts, drinks, wine, and cassis liqueur.

Home use tips: For dropsy, urine retention and rheumatism. Boil 2
teaspoonsful in 250 ml water. Drink 2–3 cups daily.

Lady's Mantle* ❀

Alchemilla

(Rose Family)

This is a genus of pretty plants with characteristically palmately lobed or
divided, toothed leaves, and clusters of tiny, yellowish green flowers. The
flowers have green sepals and lack petals. There are many species in
Europe and they can only be reliably identified by the expert, using
detailed floras. Illustrated here are:

Alpine Lady's Mantle° ❀ (*Alchemilla alpina*, 291)

This is quite easy to identify, with 5–7 narrow leaflets and silvery underside
to the leaves.

Flowering season: June–Aug

Habitat: Mountain grassland, rocks and scree.

Distribution: Mountains of Europe. In BI, mainly SW Ireland, Scotland
and Lake District.

Alchemilla monticola° ☒ (292)

This a hairy plant, growing to about 30 cm. The leaves are rounded,
3–10 cm across, with 7–9 toothed lobes.

Flowering season: May–Sep

Habitat: Poor meadows and pastures.

Distribution: Europe, E to Siberia. Common in much of C and E Europe,
but quite rare in England (found in Weardale and Teesdale).

For both the above species:

Active ingredients: Tannins, bitters, some essential oil.

Uses: An infusion regulates periods. Leaf decoction treats sore eyes, sore
skin, and staunches bleeding.

Further uses: Young leaves can be added to salads. Leaves yield a green dye.

Home use tips: An infusion to improve the complexion and regulate
periods. Boil 1 teaspoonful in 250 ml water, infuse for 10–15 minutes.
Drink 1–3 cups daily.

292

293 Carob ✿   *Ceratonia siliqua*
(Pea Family)

Evergreen bush or tree to 10 m tall, with stout trunk and grey-brown bark. Leaves leathery, compound, with 2–5 pairs of large obovate leaflets, each 4–5 cm long, shiny green above and reddish-brown beneath. Flowers very small, on all male or mixed spikes on old wood. Calyx 5-lobed. Corolla absent. Male flowers with 5 long stamens. Fruit a large flat, leathery pod, 10–20 cm long and 2 cm wide; at first green and fleshy, ripening and drying to dark brown, containing large shiny brown seeds.

Flowering season: May–Oct

Habitat: Dry hillsides, scrub.

Distribution: Mediterranean; Near East. Widely cultivated, mainly in N Africa, Greece and Cyprus.

Active ingredients: Sugar, pectin, mucilage, tannins, organic acids.

Uses: In many preparations to treat stomach disorders and diarrhoea.

Further uses: Formerly as food; now mainly as fodder. Pod pulp is eaten as a sweet, and used as a caffeine-free chocolate substitute, as well as to make various soft and alcoholic drinks.

Note: Also called Locust Bean, these pods are the 'locusts' eaten with honey by St John the Baptist. The regularly sized seeds were used as weights by jewellers – hence the term 'carat'.

294 Annual Mercury* ☠   *Mercurialis annua*
(Spurge Family)

Small leafy and bushy, almost hairless annual, to 40 cm tall. Leaves opposite, stalked, narrowly oval and pointed, with coarse teeth. Plant dioecious. Male plants with many-flowered spikes; each flower small, green and 3-lobed, with 8–12 stamens. Female flowers solitary or in groups of 2 or 3, with 2-celled ovary. Fruit a 2-celled capsule. Fruit stalk shorter than fruit.

Flowering season: May–Oct

Habitat: Rich, weedy habitats, including gardens and fields.

Distribution: Europe; Asia; N Africa. In BI, possibly native; commonest in the south.

Active ingredients: Saponins, essential oil, amines.

Uses: In homeopathy to treat rheumatism and mouth infections.

NB: Poisonous. Do not prepare at home.

Similar species: Dog's Mercury°
☠ (*M. perennis*) is a single-stemmed plant to 40 cm tall. Leaves opposite, coarsely toothed and lanceolate, about 4–12 cm long and crowded together towards top of stem. Fruit stalk several times longer than fruit. Found in shady deciduous woods, mainly on calcareous soils.

a
female flower

M. perennis
male flower
b

293

294

Buckthorn* ☠ ♟

Rhamnus cathartica

(Buckthorn Family)

Bushy, usually spiny deciduous shrub or small, rounded tree to 8 m tall.
Leaves alternate or nearly opposite. Stalk 1–2.5 cm long; blade broadly
elliptical, 3–6 cm long, with a short point. Leaf margin finely toothed,
usually hairless. Leaves have 3 or 4 pairs of curved lateral veins joining
together towards the tip. Flowers in groups of 2–8, in the leaf axils.
Perianth 4-partite, yellow-green, small and inconspicuous. Sepals narrow
and triangular, 2–3 mm long. Petals linear and pointed, twice as long as
sepals. Stamens 4. Fruit a round, pea-sized, berry with 2–4 seeds, blue-black
and juicy when ripe.

Flowering season: May–June

Habitat: Scrub, hedges and open woods, fens.

Distribution: Most of Europe; W Asia. In BI locally common in England,
scattered in Wales and Ireland, and rare elsewhere.

Active ingredients: Anthraquinone compounds, flavone-glycosides.

Uses: In various medical preparations as mild laxative.

NB: Poisonous. Do not prepare at home.

Sea Buckthorn* ✾

Hippophae rhamnoides

(Sea Buckthorn Family)

Much-branched shrub or small tree, to 6 m tall, with thorny, smooth,
red-brown branches. Shoots with silver-grey hairs. Leaves alternate,
short-stalked. Blade long and narrow, 2–7 cm long and at most 1 cm wide,
with entire margin and mealy on both sides. Dark green above, silvery or
copper-red below. Plant dioecious. Male flowers yellow-brown, about
3 mm across, stalkless, in rounded clusters. Sepals 2, petals absent. Stamens
4. Female flowers tube-shaped. Fruit juicy and edible (but sour); an oval,
orange, single-seeded berry-like achene, about 6–8 mm long.

Flowering season: Apr–May

Habitat: On mainland Europe from the coast to subalpine levels; pioneer
scrub on dunes, river gravel, in gravel pits and open pine woods. In BI
mainly coastal (especially dunes).

Distribution: Europe and Asia. In BI possibly native only in E England, but
widely planted.

Active ingredients: Vitamins, including large amounts of vitamin C,
minerals, fruit acids, sugar, flavonoids, anthocyanins.

Uses: Useful vitamin supplement for colds, and in convalescence. Young
berries used to treat diarrhoea and dysentery.

Further uses: Fruits used to make juice and jelly. Yields a yellow dye.

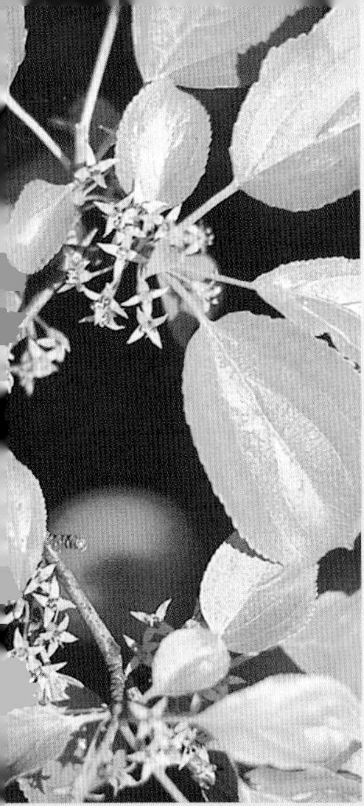

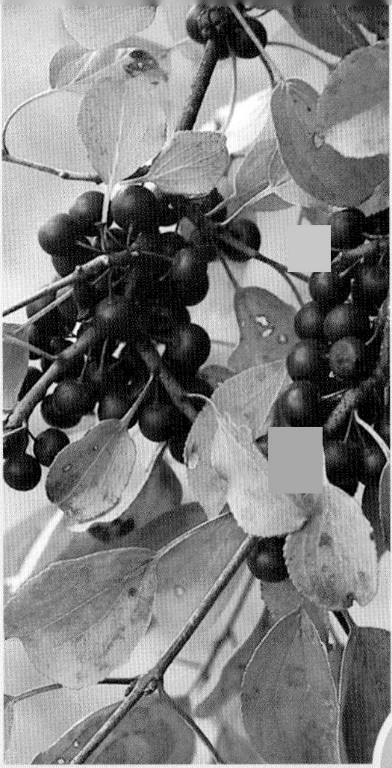

295

296

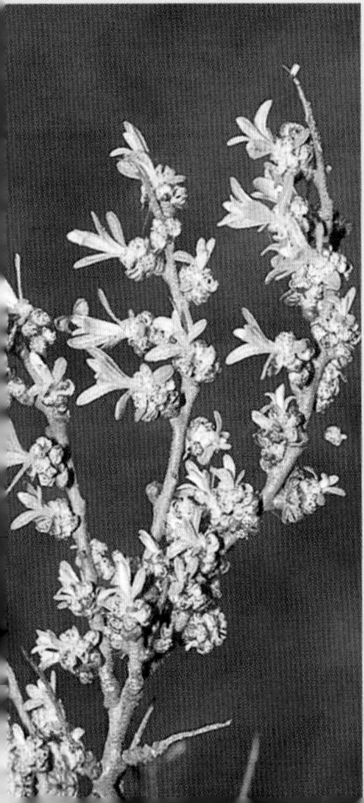

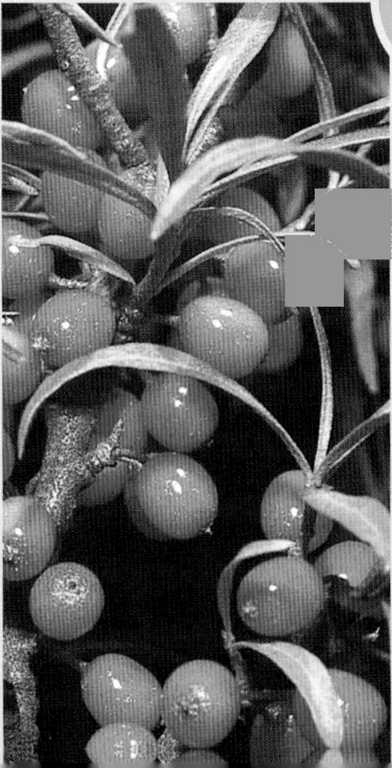

297

298

Garden Parsley* ⊛

Petroselinum crispum

(Carrot Family)

Hairless biennial with characteristic aroma, growing to 1 m tall, in some forms developing a fleshy taproot. Stems erect, often hollow, branched in upper half. Leaves stalked, 3-pinnate, with triangular outline and diamond shaped, coarsely toothed leaflets. Leaves curled in many cultivated varieties. Flowers (photo top right) in long-stalked umbels with 10–20 spokes. Bracts 1–3, often leaf-like; bracteoles 6–8, very narrow. Petals 5, greenish-yellow. Fruit oval, 2.5–3 mm long, with fine ridges.

Flowering season: June–July

Habitat: Rich, moist soils. Much cultivated. Waste ground, tips.

Distribution: E Mediterranean. In BI introduced; scattered.

Active ingredients: Essential oil, apiine (a flavone-glycoside), furocoumarins.

Uses: To treat urinary infection, kidney stones, water retention and menstrual disorders. Leaf infusion is an eye, hair and skin tonic. Aids digestion and relieves rheumatism.

Further uses: As culinary herb. Root eaten in soups and stews.

NB: Do not use wild form, because of risk of confusion with poisonous species.

Note: Three mains forms are grown: Curled Parsley; Uncurled Parsley; Hamburg Parsley. The latter has an edible, turnip-like taproot.

Garden Angelica* ⊛

Angelica archangelica

(Carrot Family)

Hairless, aromatic perennial to 2 m tall, with taproot. Stem up to arm-thickness at base, furrowed. Basal leaves 60–90 cm long, 3-pinnate, with long hollow stalk. Leaflets narrowly ovate, 5–8 cm long, toothed. Flowers in umbels to 15 cm across with 20–40 spokes. Bracts absent. Bracteoles many, linear. Petals greenish, 1–1.5 mm long, elliptic. Fruit pale yellow, compressed, 5–8 mm long, with 3 dorsal ridges and winged lateral ridges.

Flowering season: July–Aug

Habitat: Pastures, riverbanks, damp sites. Occasionally cultivated.

Distribution: N Europe; N Asia. In BI introduced; scattered and local, notably along the Thames.

Active ingredients: Essential oil, tannins, bitters, furocoumarins, sugar.

Uses: To treat digestive problems.

Further uses: Stalks can be candied for use in cakes. Shoots added to salads, stems and roots as vegetables and the seeds in pastries. Oil used in some gins, vermouths and perfumes. Crushed leaves said to reduce travel sickness.

Home use tips: For loss of appetite: Boil 2 teaspoonsful in 250 ml water for 2 minutes. Drink 2–3 cups daily. As bath, for rheumatism and aching muscles: Boil 100 g in 1 l water for 15 minutes. Add to bath water twice weekly.

Similar species: The native Wild Angelica*(*A. sylvestris*, 212) is much commoner in BI. It has purple-tinged stems and is less aromatic.

NB: Use only bought preparations, because of risk of confusion with poisonous species.

Ivy*

Hedera helix

(Ivy Family)

Woody evergreen, climbing by means of short stem-roots. Stem branched, woody towards base. Leaves alternate, stalked, leathery, dark green and shiny above with palmate veins. Leaves on vegetative stems 3–5 lobed, rather tough. Leaves on flowering stems simple and less stiff. Flowers small, 5-partite, in small, dense rounded clusters. Calyx with short teeth. Petals 5, fleshy, oval, pointed, 3–4 mm long, brown outside, green inside. Stamens 5. Fruit a round, blue-black berry, 8–10 mm across.

Flowering season: Sep–Dec

Habitat: Trees, rocks, cliffs, hedges, gardens (many garden varieties); often in shade.

Distribution: Europe, except far N; Asia.

Active ingredients: Saponins, notably hederasaponin C; alkaloids; iodine.

Uses: Medicinally in various preparations to treat coughs, whooping cough, and bronchitis. In homeopathy for over-active thyroid, gallbladder complaints and bronchial asthma. Leaves make a poultice to treat neuralgia, rheumatism and sciatica. Also reduces fevers and expels worms.

NB: Poisonous. Do not prepare.

Common Ash* ⊛

Fraxinus excelsior

(Ash Family)

Deciduous tree to 40 m tall, with rounded or oval crown. Bark pale grey and smooth at first, becoming dark and ridged. Twigs thick, with large, black buds. Leaves opposite, to 35 cm long, pinnate, with 9–15 leaflets. Leaflets narrowly elliptical and pointed, 4–10 cm long, unstalked (except for terminal leaflets), with finely toothed margins. Trees may be monoecious or dioecious, and the flowers hermaphrodite or unisexual. Flowers in many-flowered panicles, at first upright, but later drooping. Individual flowers are inconspicuous and lack petals. Stamens 2(3), brownish-red to violet. Ovary with 2-lobed stigma. Fruits are clusters of the familiar winged achenes ('keys'), each 2–4 cm long, ripening from green to brown. Ripe keys stay on the tree for a long time.

Flowering season: May

Habitat: Mixed deciduous woods, scrub, hedgerows. Often alongside rivers or small streams in hills. Commonly planted in parks and at roadsides.

Distribution: Europe, Turkey.

Active ingredients: Flavonoids, coumarins, bitters, essential oil.

Uses: As a medicinal tea, for rheumatism, and to aid kidney problems.

Further uses: Young ash keys can be pickled as a caper substitute.

Home use tips: Medicinal tea. Boil 1 teaspoonful in 250 ml water; infuse for 3 minutes. Drink 3 cups daily. For rheumatism drink 2 cups daily, for at least 2 weeks.

Deadly Nightshade* ☠ ✖   *Atropa belladonna*

(Nightshade Family)

Bushy perennial to 1.5 m tall with erect stems. Leaves alternate or paired, short-stalked, entire, ovate to elliptic, to 15 cm long. Flower stalked and solitary in leaf axils; drooping. Calyx 5-partite, with oval, pointed lobes. Corolla bell-shaped, 2.5–3.5 cm long, opening into 5 lobes; brownish-violet on outside, yellow-green with red veins on inside. Fruit a shiny, black, cherry-sized berry, 1–1.5 cm across.

Flowering season: June–Aug

Habitat: Light woods, clearings, scrub, rough ground; around old buildings.

Distribution: Europe; Asia. In BI, scattered, mainly in C and E England.

Active ingredients: Alkaloids, notably hyoscyamine, atropine and scopolamine.

Uses: To treat cramp-like intestinal and urinary pains. In homeopathy for headaches. Narcotic and sedative. Atropine enlarges the pupil of the eye and is still sometimes used for eye examinations.

NB: Deadly poisonous. Do not use.

Note: The name 'belladonna' comes from the fact that an extract of the berry was once used in Italy to enhance beauty by enlarging the pupil of the eye.

Henbane* ☠ ✖   *Hyoscyamus niger*

(Nightshade Family)

Downy, sticky annual or biennial with unpleasant smell, growing to 80 cm tall. Leaves alternate, ovate or oblong, deeply toothed; lower leaves stalked, upper leaves encircling stem at base. Flowers yellow-brown, with purple veins; solitary, in leaf axils, mainly towards the top of the plant. Calyx bell-shaped, sharply 5-toothed. Corolla funnel-shaped, deeply lobed.

Flowering season: June–Oct

Habitat: Waste ground, farmyards, old buildings, coastal sand or shingle.

Distribution: Europe; Asia; N Africa. In BI, scattered, mainly southern.

Active ingredients: Alkaloids hyoscyamine, scopolamine, atropine; tannins.

Uses: To treat asthma, colic and Parkinson's disease. Reduces muscular tension before surgery. In homeopathy for coughs and spasms. Formerly widely used as sedative and painkiller.

NB: Deadly poisonous. Do not use.

Common Figwort* ✖   *Scrophularia nodosa*

(Figwort Family)

Erect perennial to 1.2 m cm tall, with rectangular stems and glandular hairs in inflorescence. Leaves opposite, short-stalked, oval, pointed and coarsely toothed. Flowers greenish or purplish-brown, in many-branched inflorescence. Calyx has short lobes, with membranous margins. Corolla inflated, 5–6 mm long, with a purple upper lip, and shorter lower lip.

Flowering season: June–July

Habitat: Damp woods, hedges; often in shade.

Distribution: Throughout Europe, except far N; Asia.

Active ingredients: Saponins, flavone-glycosides, alkaloids, cardiac glycosides.

Uses: In homeopathy for scrofula (hence Latin name), swollen glands and eczema. Has diuretic and pain-relieving properties.

NB: Poisonous. Do not prepare.

308 Greater Plantain*

Plantago major

(Plantain Family)

Weakly hairy perennial to 40 cm tall. Leaves in basal rosette. Leaves long, broadly oval, rounded or heart-shaped at base and 5–9 veined. Spike dense, cylindrical and up to 10 cm long, reaching even 20 cm in fruit. Sepals 4, unfused. Corolla yellowish, tube-shaped, with 4 lobes. Fruit a capsule, to 4 mm long, usually with 8 seeds.

Flowering season: June–Oct

Habitat: Footpaths, damp meadows, pastures, lawns.

Distribution: Throughout Europe. Spread worldwide.

Active ingredients: Mucilage, tannin, aucubine, vitamin C, silicic acid.

Uses: In homeopathy for toothache, middle-ear infections and bed-wetting.

Similar species: Hoary Plantain* (*P. media*) has elliptic leaves, narrowing gradually into the stalk. Found on dry, especially calcareous, grassland.

Note: Greater Plantain is a classic ruderal plant, colonising waste ground and footpaths, and extremely tolerant of trampling. The small seeds cling to the feet of animals and people, and thus get dispersed. In N America this species followed soon after the Europeans appeared and came to be known to the Native Americans as 'White Man's Footsteps'.

309 Ribwort Plantain*

Plantago lanceolata

(Plantain Family)

Hairless or slightly hairy perennial to 50 cm tall. Leaves lanceolate, in basal rosette, erect, with obvious longitudinal veins. Flowerheads rounded at first, becoming cylindrical, on long stalks. Calyx and corolla 4-lobed. Fruit a 2-seeded capsule.

Flowering season: Apr–Sep

Habitat: Meadows, pastures, footpaths, roadsides, lawns.

Distribution: Throughout Europe. Spread worldwide.

Active ingredients: Mucilage, tannin, aucubine, vitamin C, silicic acid.

Uses: To treat coughs, colds and bronchial inflammation. Fresh leaves expel catarrh.

Home use tips: For coughs and colds. Infuse 1–2 teaspoonsful in 250 ml boiling water for 15 minutes. Drink 2–3 cups daily. Also on poultice, mixed with Chamomile tea (see 241), to treat wounds, insect stings and itchy rashes.

310 Glandular Plantain*

Plantago afra

(Plantain Family)

Glandular hairy annual, to 40 cm tall, with branching stem. Leaves opposite, linear-lanceolate, 6–8 cm long and 3–4 mm wide, sessile. Flowerheads in the axils of upper leaves, each 1–1.5 cm long, on stalks 5–8 cm long. Sepals 4, free. Corolla 4 mm long, tube-shaped, with 4 pointed lobes. Fruit a 2-seeded capsule, 3–3.5 mm long.

Flowering season: June–Sep

Habitat: Waste land, tips.

Distribution: S and E Europe; W Asia. In BI, introduced (grain and bird-seed alien), scattered.

Active ingredients: Mucilage, tannins, fatty oil, aucubine.

Uses: To treat intestinal problems and chronic constipation.

310

Mugwort*

Artemisia vulgaris

(Daisy Family)

Branched perennial, to about 1.3 m tall, with an unpleasant smell. Stem angled, branched and weakly hairy. Leaves green and hairless above, covered with grey or white felty hairs below; divided, with lanceolate, toothed lobes. Lower leaves stalked, upper leaves stalkless. Flowerheads very small, ovoid, 3–4 mm long and arranged in a many-headed panicle. Flowers yellowish or reddish-brown.

Flowering season: July–Sep

Habitat: Footpaths, waste ground, river banks.

Distribution: Europe; N Africa. Almost worldwide. In BI common in lowlands.

Active ingredients: Essential oil, bitters.

Uses: Digestive aid, to treat diarrhoea and regulate menstruation. Repels insects.

Further uses: Sometimes used as a herb, and occasionally to flavour beer.

Home use tips: For loss of appetite, and diarrhoea. Infuse 1 teaspoonful in 250 ml boiling water for 1–2 minutes. Drink 1–3 cups daily.

Butterbur*

Petasites hybridus

(Daisy Family)

Erect dioecious perennial with flower spikes to 40 cm tall, reaching up to 1 m tall when in fruit. Plant with grey, felty hairs. Leaves stalked, very large and up to 60 cm across, heart-shaped and toothed. Stem leaves scale-like. Flowerheads in dense cylindrical spikes. Florets tubular, with reddish corolla (photo lower left). Female florets about 5 mm across, male about 1 cm across. Fruit with white, hairy pappus, to 1 cm long.

Flowering season: Mar–May

Habitat: Riverbanks and streamsides, wet alder scrub, damp waste ground.

Distribution: Most of Europe, except far N; N and W Asia. In BI, male plants are locally common, while female plants occur mainly in N and C England.

Active ingredients: Mucilage, petasitin, essential oil.

Uses: Acts as relaxant and painkiller for stomach and intestinal ailments. Leaves and flowers reduce bleeding, and swollen veins. In homeopathy to treat coughs, hoarseness, urinary problems and lower back pain.

Note: The leaves of Colt's-foot may cause confusion (79/80).

Botany in Brief

The flowering plants form the largest group in the plant kingdom, with more than 250,000 species so far described. Although they exist in a bewildering variety of forms, they are all built according to a similar plan, consisting of the three basic organs – root, shoot and leaf.

Longevity

Botanists distinguish between annuals, biennials and perennials. *Annuals* complete their life-cycle (germination, growth, flowering and seed production) within a year. *Biennials* grow without flowering in the first year, coming into flower in the second. Both these groups are herbs which flower only once, produce seeds, and then die. *Perennials* flower for several or many years in succession. Some perennials have herbaceous above-ground foliage, and die back after producing seeds. Others die back to a woody stem-base, sending out fresh shoots the following spring. In *woody plants* (trees and shrubs) the whole shoot system is woody and permanent.

THE ROOT

Roots serve to anchor a plant and to facilitate the uptake of water and mineral salts. They normally grow deep in the soil and are leafless. The *main or tap root* is normally vertical. From this grow *lateral roots*, which may themselves branch, and in this way the full root system develops. Many plants have swollen roots which contain stores of food.

THE SHOOT

The stem is made up of *internodes*, separated by *nodes*. The leaves arise at these nodes, which are often somewhat thickened. Sometimes the stem remains unbranched, but there are usually *side branches* as well, emerging from buds in the leaf axils. The side branches may themselves branch, resulting in a *shoot system*.

Shoots continue to grow at the tip, and develop new leaves, with buds in the axils, which can grow into branches. The shoot can either be hairless, or it may carry hairs of various kinds. The following hair types can be distinguished by their texture:
bristles: simple, stiff, often pricking
felted: matted together, soft
downy: scattered, delicate
rough: strong, long, patent
silky: appressed, soft, shiny
woolly: soft, curved, often long
ciliate: thin, lash-like
glandular hairs: stalked glands

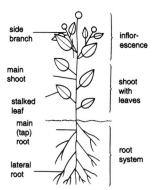

Schematic diagram of a plant

THE LEAF

Leaf position

Leaves grow as lateral appendages of the stem, from nodes. When there is a single leaf at each node, and successive leaves are not directly above each other, we speak of *alternate* leaves. If there are two leaves, one at each side of the node, they are termed *opposite*, although the pairs of leaves at successive nodes may be set at right angles to each other. When there are three or more leaves at each node, they are described as *whorled*, or in whorls.

Leaf structure

A fully developed leaf consists of the *blade*, the *leafstalk* (petiole), and *leaf base*. Sometimes there is no leafstalk, in which case the leaf is termed *sessile*, or unstalked; otherwise it is known as *petiolate*, or stalked. The leaf base is often inconspicuous, but sometimes has a *leaf sheath*, or *stipules* associated with it. Unstalked leaves may

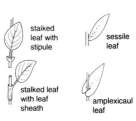

narrow towards the stem. Those partially encircling the stem with the leaf bases are called *sheathing* leaves. In other cases, the leaf base may have blunt or pointed extensions at either side of the stem (*amplexicaul*), or even completely encircle and fuse with the stem (*perfoliate*). In *decurrent* leaves, the leaf blade extends some distance down the sides of the stem.

Leaf shapes

Leaves can be many different *shapes*, and these shapes are often important taxonomic characters. There are *simple* leaves with undivided blade, and *compound* leaves. Some have *parallel* or curved veins, without a central midrib; others have *pinnate* veins, with an obvious midrib and lateral veins. A leaf can have any one of a number of shapes, including:
linear, lanceolate, elliptic, ovate, hastate (spear-shaped), *reniform* (kidney-shaped), *cordate* (heart-shaped), *rhombic, spatulate* or spathulate (spoon-shaped) or *sagittate* (arrow-shaped) (see page 1).

There are also differences in leaf *margins*, including:
entire, crenate (bluntly toothed margins), *serrate* (serrated), *dentate* (toothed), *sinuate/undulate* (wavy margins), *pinnately lobed*, or *palmately lobed* (see front-paper).

There is just as much variation in the *shapes of compound leaves*. These leaves consist of several separate leaflets. When the leaflets are paired along the central stem, the leaves are known as *pinnate* (*imparipinnate* if there is a terminal leaflet and *paripinnate* if not) (see front-paper).

THE INFLORESCENCE

That part of the stem which carries the flowers is known as the
inflorescence. In rare cases, a shoot has just a single flower at its tip, but
more often there are several or many flowers, arranged in a number of
different ways (see front-paper).

A *spike* is a flowerhead in which the individual flowers are stalkless. It can
be short and dense, or long and loose. A *raceme* is similar, but consists of
stalked flowers. A *panicle* is an inflorescence whose main branches are
themselves branched. In an *umbel*, the flower stalks are of equal length and
arise from the same point on the stem. Umbels are often surrounded at the
base by an *involucre* of bracts. Umbels are often *compound*, with several
partial umbels on stalks of equal length. A *head* consists of many unstalked
or short-stalked flowers growing close together at the end of a stem. The
particularly densely-clustered head of composites is known as a *capitulum*.
In it, the individual flowers grow from the expanded end of a stem and are
surrounded by an involucre.

THE FLOWER

Flower structure

The flower is a thickened shoot which carries the reproductive parts of the
plant. Its individual parts can be interpreted as modified leaves. The
perianth consists either of *perianth segments*, or of *sepals* and *petals*. The
male part of the flower (*androecium*) consists of the *stamens*; the female
part (*gynoecium*) consists of the *ovary*, *style* and *stigma*, together known as
the *pistil*.

The perianth

The parts of a flower usually have a circular arrangement, and may
sometimes overlap each other. The *perianth segments* make up the outer
(lower) ring. More commonly, these are differentiated into an outer ring of
usually green sepals (the *calyx*), and an inner ring of usually coloured petals
(the *corolla*). The *sepals* may be either free or fused together. The fused
part is called the *calyx tube* or *calyx cup*, with free *calyx teeth* or *calyx
lobes*. Sometimes the calyx is surrounded by an *epicalyx* of bracts.

The *petals*, collectively called the *corolla*, form the next ring. Their
colour serves to attract pollinating insects, as do the scent and the sugary
nectar secreted by the *nectaries*. Sometimes there is a *spur* at the base of
the petals, which may act as a reservoir for nectar. The petals may also be
free, or fused together. Some flowers, particularly those pollinated by wind,
have reduced petals or may even lack petals altogether.

Reproductive parts

Next in from the perianth is a ring or rings of *stamens*. Each stamen
consists of a thin *filament* and an *anther*, the latter containing the *pollen*. In
the centre of the flower is the *pistil* (gynoecium). This consists of at least
one *carpel*, often more, either free or fused. The pistil is divided into *ovary*,

style and *stigma*. The ovary may be *superior* (that is above the perianth base) or *inferior* (below the perianth base). It may also be *intermediate* in position.

Symmetry

If a flower has more than 1 axis of symmetry it is known as *radially symmetrical (actinomorphic)*. Flowers with a single axis of symmetry are *bilaterally symmetrical (zygomorphic)*, and the perianth is often divided into an *upper-* and a *lower-lip*. Flowers which are only male or female (contain either only stamens or only carpels) are called *unisexual*.

THE FRUIT

The fruit develops from the *ovary*, after pollination. It protects the seeds until they are ripe and often also has particular adaptations for seed dispersal. Its morphology is dependent, among other things, on the number of carpels and their arrangement. There are many different kinds of fruit (see end-paper).

Dehiscent fruits

These are fruits which open to release the seeds. A *follicle* develops from a single carpel and splits open along one side only. A *legume* opens along both sides. A *capsule* is formed from more than one carpel. There are many types of capsule, including those with pores, teeth, or which open along clefts, or which split around the middle. One type of capsule is the *siliqua*, which consists of two carpels whose fused edges carry the seeds, and a central, papery partition. The siliqua opens when the two outer edges bend upwards away from the partition. Siliquas less than three times as long as broad are called *siliculas*.

Indehiscent fruits

These are fruits which do not open, and which are therefore dispersed with their seeds. A *nut* is usually single-seeded and has a hard covering. A small, indehiscent, single-seeded nut may be called an *achene*. Fleshy fruits with a central hard, "stone" seed are called *drupes*. In a *berry*, the whole fruit wall is fleshy. Some fruits split into many parts when ripe. *Multiple*, or *compound* fruits develop many, separate carpels. Indehiscent fruits may have special modifications for dispersal. Examples are *winged fruits*, and those with feathery outgrowths (e.g. the *pappus* which develops from the modified calyx in composites).

PLANT COLLECTION, PREPARATION AND USE

Collection

Medicinal plants, with their valuable chemical compounds, are a gift of nature, and many of them have been used for centuries in traditional medicine for treating particular complaints, whilst others have been forgotten. Nowadays we are witnessing a revival of interest in natural medicine. Nevertheless, the gathering and use of herbs should not be undertaken lightly and carries with it great responsibility, because mistakes are possible and confusion with dangerous species is a risk. **Medicinal plants should only be gathered when identification is certain. If there is even the slightest doubt, do not use self-gathered herbs as medicine, but buy a commercially produced preparation.**

The prime consideration should be conservation, and a stand of a particular medicinal species should never be harvested in its entirety. **Rare species should never be collected.** Be careful not to damage natural habitats and collect from as few plants as possible.

Harvest only fresh and healthy material. Perennials should always be cut fairly high so that they can sprout again. Fruits should be gathered when ripe, and roots dug up in spring or autumn. But remember it is illegal to uproot any wild plant without permission.

Preparation

Freshly gathered plant material should be prepared so that it can be used as a medicine throughout the year. Natural drying is suitable for leaves, flowers and delicate herbs. They should be spread out on clean paper (not newsprint) in a shady, well ventilated spot, and turned over from time to time. Plant fragments which contain volatile essential oils should always be dried in this way since they lose their potency if dried too rapidly at high temperature.

Plant parts which are difficult to dry, such as fleshy fruits and roots, need to be dried out by heating. This method is also suitable for Elder flowers. Ideally, leave them out for a day or two in a well ventilated spot, then dry in an oven or over a radiator at a temperature of up to 45 degrees C.

Storing herbal medicines

When thoroughly dry (twigs should snap easily, berries and roots should no longer be soft, even inside) check carefully and discard any pieces that are mouldy. Then the material is usually divided up into small pieces, suitable for use as infusions, if appropriate. Ideally, herbal medicines should be stored in airtight, opaque containers. This is important because light can alter the chemical composition and efficacy. Do not forget to label all containers clearly, with the contents and date of harvest. Many herbal remedies gradually lose their effectiveness, and should not therefore be stored for long periods.

Uses of medicinal plants

Tea and other infusions are some of the oldest and most useful forms in which to take herbal medicine. An infusion is a watery solution, prepared by using either hot or cold water. Different herbs require different methods of preparation to attain their optimal effectiveness, and details of these are given in the entries under the section *tips on home preparation*. In all cases infusions should be freshly made; only enough to last a single day. Fruits, such as Caraway, Fennel and Aniseed, which contain essential oils, should be crushed or ground before use in such preparations. Then the infusion should be strained, and unless otherwise indicated it should be sipped hot, before or after a meal. For **children**, the same recipes can be used, but only half a cup should be taken.

Infusions can be used **externally** as well, and this includes use as a gargle, when the temperature should not exceed 35 degrees C. For **poultices**, for example in treating wounds or eczema, the infusion should be undiluted and at body temperature. Soak a cotton wool pad with the infusion, lay this on the area to be treated and secure it with a well aerated linen bandage. Never wrap with an airtight bandage, such as plastic. In the case of hands or feet, these should be bathed in an infusion at 35–40 degrees C for 10–15 minutes.

For a full herbal bath, one needs correspondingly more herbal extract – perhaps 100 to 300 g, according to the recipe, in 2–3 litres of water, added to the bath water after sieving. Optimal bathing time is around 15 minutes, at a water temperature of 35 degrees C, and ideally this should be followed by a period of relaxation. Inhalations are another form of use. In this case a handful of prepared herb is brought to a simmer in about a litre of water. Then the head and container are covered with a cloth and the herb-infused steam breathed in through nose and mouth for 5–10 minutes.

Important active ingredients

Active herbal compounds belong to a number of different classes of chemical. They are products of plant metabolism and as such may be found either throughout the tissues of a plant, or stored in specific organs. Most herbs contain several active chemicals, which may work together synergistically (more effectively than each would on its own). Plants may also contain other substances which may be neutral in terms of their effects, or they may support the effects of the active ingredients, or they may in some cases be antagonistic. Some active chemicals produce such strong effects on the body that we speak of them as poisons. However, many of these substances can be used as medicines in standardised doses and in the hands of a qualified doctor. **Medicinal plants which contain poisons should never be used by the amateur!**

Essential oils are volatile and usually have a characteristic, often aromatic smell. They are virtually insoluble in water, but are easily taken up by water vapour or steam. They are most effective on skin and mucous membranes and work well as expectorants. Medicines with essential oils are therefore particularly suitable for mouth and bronchial complaints, but also find a use in digestive disorders, to stimulate the appetite, as spices, and in some cases in aromatherapy. The umbellifer and legume families contain many plants with essential oils.

Alkaloids are a group of basic organic compounds containing nitrogen. They tend to have strong and rather varied physiological effects. Many are poisonous, and this group includes some of the most deadly poisons known. Preparations containing alkaloids should therefore not be handled by the amateur. In medicine, however, they are extremely useful, and examples are codeine and morphine, produced from the Opium Poppy. Alkaloids are also present in coffee and tea (caffeine), tobacco leaves (nicotine) and are amongst the strongest drugs (opium, morphine, and the derived heroin). Medicinal plants rich in alkaloids can be found particularly amongst members of the lily, buttercup, poppy and nightshade families.

Bitters are a mixed group of bitter-tasting compounds. They tend to cause an increase in digestive secretions and gall-bladder activity. In short they improve digestion and appetite, and also affect putrefaction and fermentation processes. Medicines containing them should be taken before meals. They are commonly found in members of the gentian, mint and composite families.

Flavonoids are often yellow coloured and are usually bound to sugars. They are found in many plants, but do not normally form the main part of a herbal medicine. They affect, amongst other things, the walls of fine blood vessels, and are therefore useful for example in treating veins, arteriosclerosis and high blood pressure. They often work synergistically with other compounds.

Tannins are found in a wide range of plants. They denature animal proteins and are used to tan leather. This property makes them particularly useful, since they can form a protective layer over infected skin or mucous membranes. This stops secretions and bleeding, whilst at the same time preventing bacteria and other particles from entering the wound or infected tissue, and lessening pain. External uses for tannin-rich medicines include treating wounds and rashes, mouth and throat inflammation and light frost-bite; internally they are used for inflammation of the stomach or intestine.

Cardiac glycosides are complex organic compounds bound to sugars. They have strong effects on heart function. Most are very poisonous and should therefore only be handled by qualified doctors. The best known are the digitalis glycosides from Foxglove which are used to stimulate the heartbeat.

Collection calendar for herbs and healing plants

A selection of species that are suitable for collection and use at home:

PLANT	PAGE	USEFUL PART	COLLECTION TIME
Agrimony	38	flowering plant	Jun–Jul
Ash	232	leaves	Jun–Aug
Avens, Wood	38	flowering plant	Jul–Aug
Bedstraw	64	flowering plant	Jun–Sep
Betony	108	flowering plant	Jul–Aug
Bilberry	98	fruits	Jul–Aug
Birch	212	leaves	May–Jun
Bistort, Common	78	root-stock	Spr/Aut
Blackthorn	144	flowers	Mar–Apr
Blackthorn	144	fruits	Sep–Nov
Bramble	144	leaves	May–Jun
Burdock	122	root	Spr/Aut
Chamomile	190	flowers	Jun–Jul
Chickweed	132	plant	Jan–Dec
Chicory	26	root and plant	Jul–Sep
Clary, Meadow	18	leaves	Apr
Clover, Hare's-foot	86	flowering plant	Jun–Aug
Clover, Red	86	flowering plant	Jun–Sep
Colt's-foot	70	flowers	Mar–Apr
Colt's-foot	70	leaves	Apr–May
Comfrey	102	root	Spr/Aut
Couch, Common	206	root-stock	Spr/Aut
Creeping Jenny	56	flowering plant	Jun–Jul
Currant, Black	224	leaves	May–Jun
Daisy	186	flowering plant	Mar–Oct
Dandelion	76	root and plant	Mar–May

PLANT	PAGE	USEFUL PART	COLLECTION TIME
Deadnettle, White	180	flowers	Jun–Aug
Dog-rose	84	fruits	Aug–Oct
Elder	184	flowers	Jun–Jul
Elder	184	fruits	Sep
Eyebright	182	flowering plant	Jun–Oct
Goldenrod	66	flowering plant	Aug–Oct
Ground-ivy	22	flowering plant	Apr–Jul
Hawkweed	76	flowering plant	Jun–Aug
Hawthorn	146	flowers	May–Jun
Heather	96	flowering plant	Jul–Oct
Hemp-nettle, Downy	60	flowering plant	Jul–Aug
Herb Robert	88	flowering plant	Jun–Sep
Hop	218	fruiting heads	Sep–Oct
Horehound, White	178	flowering plant	Jun–Aug
Juniper	202	berries	Oct–Nov
Lady's Mantle	224	plant	Apr–Jul
Lavender	20	flowers	Jun–Aug
Lime	46	flowers	Jun
Lungwort	16	flowering plant	Mar–May
Mallow	92	leaves, flowers	Jun–Jul
Marjoram	110	plant	Jun–Aug
Mayweed, Scented	190	flowers	Jun–Jul
Meadowsweet	142	flowering plant	Jun–Jul
Milkwort	14	flowering plant	May–Jul
Mugwort	238	flowering plant	Jul–Aug
Mullein	60	flowers	Jul–Aug
Nettle	216	plant	May–Jun
Oak	212	bark	Mar–Apr
Pansy, Wild	50	flowering plant	May–Aug
Pine, Scots	200	shoots	May–Jun

PLANT	PAGE	USEFUL PART	COLLECTION TIME
Plantain, Ribwort	236	leaves	May–Jun
Raspberry	144	leaves	May–Jun
Rosemary	20	leaves	Jan–Dec
Rowan	148	fruits	Aug–Oct
Sage	18	leaves	Apr
Sanicle	158	flowering plant	Jun
Scabious, Devil's-bit	24	root	Oct–Nov
Shepherd's-purse	138	flowering plant	Mar–Oct
Silverweed	40	flowering plant	May–Sep
Sorrel, Common	220	plant	Apr–May
Speedwell, Heath	24	flowering plant	Jun–Aug
St John's-wort	46	flowering plant	Jun–Jul
Strawberry, Wild	142	leaves	May–Jun
Thyme, Large	116	flowering plant	Jun–Jul
Thyme	116	plant	Jul–Aug
Tormentil	40	rootstock	Spr/Aut
Valerian, Common	118	root	Sep–Oct
Vetch, Kidney	44	flowering plant	Jun–Aug
Violet, Sweet	12	flowering plant	Mar–Apr
Watercress	140	fresh plant	Spr
Wormwood	70	flowering plant	Jun–Aug
Yarrow	188	flowering plant	Jun–Sep

Index

THE PHOTOGRAPHS

THE AUTHOR

Dieter Podlech is a Professor in the Institute for Systematic Botany at the Ludwig-Maximilians University in Munich, Germany. He is a contributor to Hegi's *Illustrated Flora of Central Europe* and co-author of Collins Nature Guide *Wild Flowers*.

THE TRANSLATOR/ADAPTOR

Martin Walters is an editor and writer with a keen interest in natural history. He has written several books on flowers and birds, and has also translated other books originally published in German, including Collins Nature Guides *Wild Flowers, Trees* and *Wild Animals*.

FLOWERS

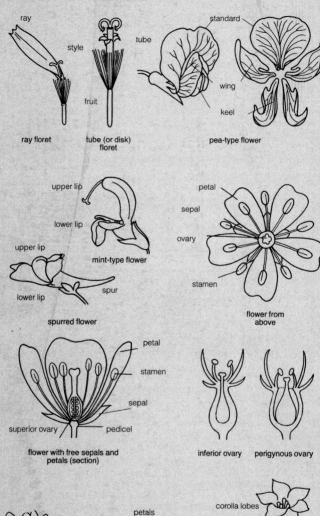

ray

style

tube

ray floret

fruit

tube (or disk) floret

standard

wing

keel

pea-type flower

upper lip

lower lip

mint-type flower

upper lip

lower lip

spur

spurred flower

petal

sepal

ovary

stamen

flower from above

petal

stamen

sepal

superior ovary

pedicel

flower with free sepals and petals (section)

inferior ovary   **perigynous ovary**

corolla (perianth)

petals

calyx

flower with free sepals and petals

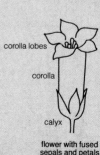

corolla lobes

corolla

calyx

flower with fused sepals and petals